AN OLD FASHIONED
KEEPBOOK™

Our
Old Fashioned
Country
Diary™
for 1982

Edited by Linda Campbell Franklin
Designed by Sara Bowman

Tree Communications, Inc.
New York

Published in the United States by
Tree Communications, Inc.,
250 Park Avenue South, New York, New York, 10003

Printed in the United States of America

Cover fabric design © 1980 VIP Fabrics Division, Cranston
Print Works Company

ISBN 0-934504-10-5

This book was typeset in Goudy Old Style by David E. Seham
Associates, Inc. Color separations were made by
Colorgraphics Inc. The paper is 70 lb Warren Olde Style,
cream, supplied by Baldwin Paper Company. The book was
printed and bound by R. R. Donnelley & Sons Company.

*I am grateful to everyone who helps make this diary better each
year by calling my attention to tidbits to share with other readers.
Editor's thanks go to Mike Billingsley and R. D. Franklin for
contributing writings. Designer's thanks go to Lauren Giber,
Rosie Mackiewicz and Carolyn Ogden for their imaginative
help. A sustained cheer goes to the Ephemera Society of
America, without whose members we would have a great deal
more trouble finding the wonderful illustrations which are such
a great part of these books.*

Write us about other books in the Keepbook™ series.

Dear Friends,

Here is the third annual KEEPBOOK diary. It is filled with all kinds of interesting new bits of information, and hundreds of new old-fashioned pictures. Something entirely different has been added to this year's diary: a look-alike contest! There are nine pictures in oval frames scattered throughout the book, all from long ago. Compare them with your own face or the faces of family and friends as they appear now or within the last five years, and see if you think you are a dead-ringer for one of the portraits. If so, please send a clear photograph to me at Tree Communications by May 4, 1982. Our Physiognomy Panel of artists, photographers and "Wow!-Look-at-that!"-ers will judge the pictures. Winners will receive two free copies of the 1983 *Old Fashioned Country Diary*, plus a side-by-side print, suitable for framing, of you and your look-alike from the past!

Have a very good year. I hope that by the end of 1982 you will have completed your own very personal version of our diary.

Yours sincerely,

Linda Campbell Franklin

Our Family's Portrait Gallery

Look-alike No. 1

New Year's

Friday January 1, 1982

Today's weather

Our Family Resolutions

How We Celebrated New Year's Eve

New Year's Eve Menu

Appetizers & Soups

Main Course

Desserts

The Way We Spent New Year's Day

A Memento of Our Day

Happy Birthday, Dear, Massa

Massa is one of the oldest captive gorillas in the world. He was born in 1930. His 51st birthday will be celebrated, as usual, on December 30, with a cake with carrot candles, and a loving rendition of "Happy Birthday." Massa, whose black hair is turning gray, has been at the Philadelphia Zoo almost all of his life, and may still be seen, as he has been over the years by hundreds of thousands of visitors.

If New Year's eve night-wind
  blow *south*,
It betokeneth warmth and growth;
If *west*, much milk, and fish
  in the sea;
If *north*, much cold, and storms
  there will be;
If *east*, the trees will bear
  much fruit;
If *north-east*, flee it man and brute.

Superstition of the Scottish Highlands, from
The Every-Day Book by William Hone, 1830

January

Sun	Mon	Tue	Wed	Thu	Fri	Sat
					1	2
3	4	5	6	7	8	9
10	11	12	13	14	15	16
17	18	19	20	21	22	23
24/31	25	26	27	28	29	30

Appointments

28 Monday

Iowa became the 29th state, 1846
President Woodrow Wilson born, 1856

29 Tuesday

President Andrew Johnson born, 1808
Texas became the 28th state, 1845

30 Wednesday

Simon Guggenheim born, 1867

31 Thursday

New Year's Eve
A Leap Second will probably be added at 11:59 p.m.

1 Friday

New Year's Day, 1982
81st annual Mummers Day Parade in Philadelphia
Rose, Orange & Sugar Bowls played. Rose Bowl 80 years old.

2 Saturday

Georgia became the 4th state, 1788

3 Sunday

Author J. R. R. Tolkein born, 1892
Alaska became the 49th state, 1959

$\mathcal{D}$ecember January

Diary

January

Sun	Mon	Tue	Wed	Thu	Fri	Sat
					1	2
3	4	5	6	7	8	9
10	11	12	13	14	15	16
17	18	19	20	21	22	23
24/31	25	26	27	28	29	30

A Fitting Sport

On January 4, 1882, Mr. Frank Frost and Mr. Fred Snow, of Bangor, Maine, skated seven miles down the Penobscot Rive in 90 minutes, and back in half an hour.

Reported in The New York Times, *January 5, 1882*

Here's Pie in Your Eye

An ancient custom on January 5, the Eve of Epiphany, at least in England, was to drink the following toast with cider, to the best-bearing apple trees in your orchard:

'*Health to thee,*
good apple tree,
Well to bear, pocket-fulls,
hat-fulls,
Peck-fulls, bushel-bag-fulls!'

Various Names for the Three Kings

Jaspar, Melchoir & Balthasar
Apellius, Amerus & Damascus
Magalath, Galgalath & Sarasin
Ator, Sator & Peratoras

Appointments

4 Monday

Louis Braille born, 1809
Utah became the 45th state, 1896

5 Tuesday

Twelfth Night
Billy Holiday recorded "When You're Smiling," 1938

6 Wednesday

Twelfth Day—Epiphany
Sherlock Holmes Birthday
New Mexico became the 47th state, 1912

7 Thursday

President Millard Fillmore born, 1800

8 Friday

Russian Christmas celebrated
Inventor Eli Whitney born, 1756

9 Saturday

Connecticut became the 5th state, 1788

10 Sunday

"Green Mountain Boy" Ethan Allen born, 1737/8
League of Nations established, 1920

January

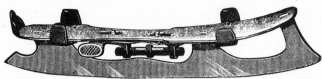

Diary

January

Sun Mon Tue Wed Thu Fri Sat
1 2
3 4 5 6 7 8 9
10 11 12 13 14 15 16
17 18 19 20 21 22 23
24/31 25 26 27 28 29 30

"The great table of nature is spread alike to all, and is amply stored with every thing necessary for the support of various families of the earth: it is owing to the superior intelligence and industry of man, that he is enabled to appropriate so large a portion of the best gifts of providence for his own subsistence and comfort; let him not then think it waste, that, in some instances, creatures inferior to him in rank are permitted to partake with him, nor let him grudge their scanty pittance."

From The Every-Day Book *by William Hone, 1830*

Perhaps a Life's Worth of Vinegar
In the last few years, some physicians in South Korea have had great success in restoring victims of carbon monoxide poisoning to consciousness with a whiff of strong vinegar. The probable explanation is that acetic acid increases the blood's ability to carry oxygen.

Appointments

11 Monday

First Treasury Secretary Alexander Hamilton born, 1757

12 Tuesday

Author Jack London born, 1876

13 Wednesday

Stephen Foster Memorial Day
Author Horatio Alger born, 1834

14 Thursday

The year 6695 on the Julian Calendar
Author John Dos Passos born, 1896

15 Friday

Drummer Gene Krupa born, 1909
Civil rights leader Martin Luther King, Jr., born, 1929

16 Saturday

Poet Robert William Service born, 1874
Baseball's Dizzy Dean born, 1911

17 Sunday

St. Anthony's Day—Blessing of Domestic Animals
Benjamin Franklin born, 1706
Comedian Mack Sennett born, 1880

January

Diary

January

Sun	Mon	Tue	Wed	Thu	Fri	Sat
					1	2
3	4	5	6	7	8	9
10	11	12	13	14	15	16
17	18	19	20	21	22	23
24/31	25	26	27	28	29	30

Banners yellow, glorious, golden,
    On its roof did float and flow,
(This—all this—was in the olden
        Time long ago;)
And every gentle air that dallied,
    In that sweet day,
Along the ramparts, plumed and pallid,
    A wingèd odor went away.

From "The Haunted Palace" by Edgar Allan Poe

"I discover this difference between indolence and laziness. Indolence is a disease of the soul, laziness of the body."

Uncle Esek, Century Magazine, 1885

Appointments

18 Monday

Captain Cook discovered Hawaii, 1778
Orator Daniel Webster born, 1782

19 Tuesday

Almanac printer Isaiaah Thomas born, 1749
General Robert E. Lee born, 1807
Author Edgar Allan Poe born, 1809

20 Wednesday

Hostages released by Iranians, 1981

21 Thursday

Stonewall Jackson born, 1824
Count Basie recorded "One O'Clock Jump," 1942

22 Friday

Pioneer film-maker D. W. Griffith born, 1875

23 Saturday

National Handwriting Day
Statesman John Hancock born, 1737

24 Sunday

Chinese New Year—Year of the Dog, 4680
"Eskimo Pie" patented by Christian Nelson of Iowa, 1922

January

Diary

"In the cavernous fire-place burns a great fire, composed of a huge green back-log, a large green fore-stick, and a high cob-work of crooked and knotty refuse-wood, ivy, hornbeam and beech. Through this the yellow flame leaps and forks, and the bluish-grey smoke flows up the ample sluice-way of the chimney. From the ends of the wood the sap fries and drips on the sizzling coals below, and flies off in angry steam."

From Margaret by Sylvester Judd, 1845

The Fox and the Goat

"A fox had fallen into a well, and thought for a long time how he might escape; when at length a Goat came around, wanting to drink, asking if the water was good, and if there was plenty of it. The Fox, dissembling the real danger of his case, replied: 'Come down, my friend; the water is so good that I cannot drink enough of it, and so abundant that it cannot be exhausted.' Upon this the Goat without any more ado leaped in; when the Fox, taking advantage of his friend's horns, as nimbly leaped out; and coolly remarked to the poor deluded Goat: 'If you had half as much brains as you have beard, you would have looked before you leaped.'

Moral

The doctrine taught us by this fable is no more than this: that we ought to consider who it is that advises us before we follow the advice."

A 19th century trade card

Appointments
25 Monday
Transcontinental telephone line opened, 1915
26 Tuesday
Michigan became the 26th state, 1837 Actor Paul Newman born, 1925
27 Wednesday
Labor leader Samuel Gompers born, 1850 Vietnam Peace Pact signed, 1973
28 Thursday
Pianist Arthur Rubenstein born, 1889 Coast Guard created, 1915
29 Friday
President William McKinley born, 1843 Kansas became the 34th state, 1861 Comedian W. C. Fields born, 1880
30 Saturday
President Franklin D. Roosevelt born, 1882
31 Sunday
Actress Tallulah Bankhead born, 1903 Canada's coldest recorded temperature, −62°F, 1947 First American earth satellite, Explorer I, launched, 1958

January

Diary

The Favorite
LUDWIG PIANO

BARLOW'S Music Store

Trenton, New Jersey

February

Sun	Mon	Tue	Wed	Thu	Fri	Sat
		1	2	3	4	5	6
7	8	9	10	11	12	13
14	15	16	17	18	19	20
21	22	23	24	25	26	27
28						

Appointments

1 Monday

Beginning of American Heart Month
National Freedom Day
Supreme Court of the U.S. met the first time, 1790

2 Tuesday

Candlemas Day
Groundhog Day
Eight baseball teams formed National League, 1876

3 Wednesday

Poet Gertrude Stein born, 1874
Illustrator Norman Rockwell born, 1894

4 Thursday

Charles A. Lindbergh born, 1902
USO founded, 1941

5 Friday

Founder of Rhode Island, Roger Williams, arrived in America, 1631
Statesman Adlai E. Stevenson born, 1900

6 Saturday

Massachusetts became the 6th state, 1788
Baseball legend Babe Ruth born, 1895
President Ronald Reagan born, 1911

7 Sunday

Author Sinclair Lewis born, 1885
The Beatles gave first American performance, N.Y.C., 1964

New Use for a Bent Pin

"We are beginning to have in society people of the cultured manner, as it is called, or polished bearing, in which the polish is the most noticeable thing about the man. Not the courtliness, the easy simplicity of the old-school gentleman, in whose presence the milkmaid was as much at her ease as the countess, but something far finer than this. These are the people of unruffled demeanor, who never forget it for a moment, and never let you forget it. Their presence is a constant rebuke to society. They are never 'jolly'; their laugh is never anything more than a well-bred smile; they are never betrayed into any enthusiasm. Enthusiasm is a sign of inexperience, of ignorance, of want of culture. They never lose themselves in any cause; they never heartily praise any man or woman or book; they are superior to all tides of feeling and all outbursts of passion. They are not even shocked at vulgarity. They are simply indifferent. They are calm, visibly calm; and it is not the eternal, majestic calmness of the Sphinx either, but a rigid, self-conscious repression. You would like to put a bent pin in their chair when they are about calmly to sit down."

From Backlog Studies by Charles Dudley Warner, 1873

February

If Candlemas-day be fair and bright,
 Winter will have another flight;
But if Candlemas-day be clouds and rain;
 Winter is gone, and will come not again.

Diary

St. Valentine's Day

Sunday February 14

Today's weather

A Loving Memento
of Our Day

Write a Song to Love

Sung to the tune of

Love Means These Things

We, the undersigned, resolve to say "I love you," each and every day.

Draw & Color a Beautiful Heart

February

Sun	Mon	Tue	Wed	Thu	Fri	Sat
		1	2	3	4	5	6
7	8	9	10	11	12	13
14	15	16	17	18	19	20
21	22	23	24	25	26	27
28						

"Not many sounds in life, and I include all urban and rural sounds, exceed in interest a *knock at the door*. It 'gives a very echo to the throne where Hope is seated.' But its issues seldom answer to this oracle within. It is so seldom that just the person we want to see comes. But of all the clamorous visitations, the welcomest in expectation is the sound that ushers in, or seems to usher in, a Valentine. As the raven himself was hoarse that announced the fatal entrance of Duncan, so the knock of the postman on this day is light, airy, confident, and befitting one that 'bringeth good tidings.' "

From The Every-Day Book *by William Hone, 1830*

Appointments

8 Monday

Boy Scouts of America founded, 1910
Actor Jack Lemmon born, 1925
Westminster Dog Show, 8th & 9th of February

9 Tuesday

President William Henry Harrison born, 1773
U.S. Weather Bureau established, 1870
Poet Amy Lowell born, 1879

10 Wednesday

Philadelphia got gas lighting, 1835

11 Thursday

Daniel Boone born, 1735
Inventor Thomas Alva Edison born, 1847

12 Friday

President Abraham Lincoln born, 1809
Naturalist Charles Darwin born, 1809
Labor leader John L. Lewis born, 1880

13 Saturday

First American public school, The Boston Latin School, founded, 1635
First American magazine, "American Magazine," published, 1741

14 Sunday

St. Valentine's Day
Brotherhood Week begins • National Wildlife Week begins
Oregon became the 33rd state, 1859; Arizona the 48th, 1912

February

"Pride is located half-way between vice and virtue, and a little of it won't hurt a saint, and a good deal of it often helps a sinner."

Uncle Esek, Century Magazine, *1885*

Diary

February

Sun	Mon	Tue	Wed	Thu	Fri	Sat
	1	2	3	4	5	6
7	8	9	10	11	12	13
14	15	16	17	18	19	20
21	22	23	24	25	26	27
28						

George "Mona Lisa" Washington
"Mrs. Wright, the celebrated wax-head modeler, had a son who was an artist. 'Wright came to Mount Vernon,'—General Washington told Watson,—'with the singular request that I should permit him to take a model of my face in plaster-of-Paris, to which I consented with some reluctance. He oiled my features over, and, placing me flat upon my back, upon a cot, proceeded to daub my face with the plaster. Whilst in this ludicrous attitude, Mrs. Washington entered the room, and, seeing my face thus overspread with the plaster, involuntarily exclaimed. Her cry excited in me a disposition to smile, which gave my mouth a slight twist, or compression of the lips, that is now observable in the busts which Wright afterward made."

A story related to the editor of Men and Manners in America One Hundred Years Ago, 1876, *by Elkanah Watson. From Scribner's Monthly, August 1876*

Appointments

15 Monday

George Washington's Birthday observed
Suffragist Susan B. Anthony born, 1820

16 Tuesday

Film-maker Robert Flaherty born, 1884
Ventriloquist Edgar Bergen born, 1903

17 Wednesday

National Congress of Mothers founded, 1896
Singer Marian Anderson born, 1902

18 Thursday

Politician Wendell Willkie born, 1892

19 Friday

Edison's phonograph patented, 1878

20 Saturday

Anti-slavery leader Frederick Douglass born, 1817
Astronaut John Glenn orbited Earth 3 times, 1962

21 Sunday

First Indian newspaper, "Cherokee Phoenix," published, 1828
Poet W. H. Auden born, 1907

February

Diary

February

Sun Mon Tue Wed Thu Fri Sat
        1 2 3 4 5 6
7 8 9 10 11 12 13
14 15 16 17 18 19 20
21 22 23 24 25 26 27
28

Appointments
22 Monday   *President George Washington born, 1732* *Poet Edna St. Vincent Millay born, 1892*
23 Tuesday   *Shrove Tuesday—Mardi Gras* *Black leader W. E. B. Du Bois born, 1868*
24 Wednesday   *Ash Wednesday—Lent begins* *Painter Winslow Homer born, 1836*
25 Thursday   *Opera singer Enrico Caruso born, 1873* *Income tax established by Constitutional Amendment XVI, 1913*
26 Friday   *Buffalo Bill (William Cody) born, 1846* *Grand Canyon became a National Park, 1919*
27 Saturday   *Poet Henry Wadsworth Longfellow born, 1807* *Consumer rights leader Ralph Nader born, 1934*
28 Sunday   *The "Vitamin C Doctor" Linus Pauling born, 1901*

Reckoning the Moveable Feasts

"Shrove Tuesday regulates most of the moveable feasts. *Shrove Tuesday* is the next after the first new moon in the month of February. If such new moon should happen on a Tuesday, the next Tuesday following is Shrove Tuesday. *Advent Sunday* is the nearest Sunday to the feast of St. Andrew, November 30, whether before or after. *Ascension Day* or *Holy Thursday* is the Thursday in Rogation Week, ie. the week following Rogation Sunday. *Ash Wednesday* is the first day in lent, the day after Shrove Tuesday. *Easter Day*, the seventh Sunday after Shrove Tuesday, is always the first Sunday after the first full moon, which happens on or next after the 21st of March. *Maunday Thursday* is the day before Good Friday. *Palm Sunday* is the sixth Sunday after Shrove Tuesday. *Pentecost* or *Whit Sunday* is the 50th day and seventh Sunday after Easter Day. *Rogation Sunday* is the fifth Sunday after Easter Sunday."

From The Every-Day Book by William Hone, 1830

February

On the Use of the Eyes

"Sit erect in your chair when reading, and as erect when writing as possible. If you bend downward you not only gorge the eyes with blood, but the brain as well, and both suffer. Hold the book at your focus; if that begins to get far away, get spectacles. Avoid reading by the flickering light of the fire. Avoid straining the eyes by reading in the gloaming. Do not read much in a railway carriage, unless in a good light. When you come to an age that suggests the wearing of spectacles, let no false modesty prevent you from getting a pair. If you have only one eye, an eyeglass will do; otherwise it is folly."

From Cassell's Magazine, circa 1889

Save Your Vision Week, March 1–7, has been proclaimed by the President since 1964.

March is Red Cross Month

	March					
Sun	Mon	Tue	Wed	Thu	Fri	Sat
	1	2	3	4	5	6
7	8	9	10	11	12	13
14	15	16	17	18	19	20
21	22	23	24	25	26	27
28	29	30	31			

Appointments

1 Monday

Easter Seal Campaign begins
National Pig Day
Ohio became the 17th state, 1807; Nebraska the 37th, 1867

2 Tuesday

Texas Independence Day
Sam Houston born, 1793

3 Wednesday

Florida became the 27th state, 1845
Alexander Graham Bell born, 1847

4 Thursday

William Penn secured grant to what is now Pennsylvania, 1681
Vermont became the 14th state, 1791

5 Friday

Bank holiday declared to save faltering banks, 1933
Treaty among 43 nations to halt spread of nuclear weapons signed, 1970

6 Saturday

Poet Elizabeth Barrett Browning born, 1806
"Harper's Weekly" published first Uncle Sam cartoon with beard, 1869

7 Sunday

Arbor Day in California
Botanist Luther Burbank born, 1849

March

Diary

March

Sun	Mon	Tue	Wed	Thu	Fri	Sat
		1	2	3	4	5	6
7	8	9	10	11	12	13
14	15	16	17	18	19	20
21	22	23	24	25	26	27
28	29	30	31			

"The lasting regret that we cannot know more of the bright, sincere, and genuine people of the world is increased by the fact that they are all different from each other. . . . Every real person—for there are persons as there are fruits that have no distinguishing flavor, mere gooseberries—has a distinct quality, and the finding it is always like the discovery of a new island to the voyager. The physical world we shall exhaust some day, having a written description of every foot of it to which we can turn; but we shall never get the different qualities of people into a biographical dictionary, and the making acquaintance with a human being will never cease to be an exciting experiment."

From Backlog Studies by Charles Dudley Warner, 1873

"Mirth is short-lived; cheerfulness never tires."

Uncle Esek, Century Magazine, 1885

Appointments

8 Monday

Jurist Oliver Wendell Holmes, Jr., born, 1841

9 Tuesday

Purim
Explorer Amerigo Vespucci born, 1451

10 Wednesday

Abolitionist leader Harriet Tubman born, c. 1820
First telephone conversation, 1876

11 Thursday

Johnny Appleseed Day—Johnny Appleseed born, 1774
The "vunnerful" Lawrence Welk born, 1903

12 Friday

The Northeast's "Great Blizzard of '88" began, 40" to 50", 1888
Girl Scouts of America founded, 1912

13 Saturday

Restauranteur Lorenzo Delmonico born, 1813
"Uncle Sam" born, sans beard, in Frank Bellew cartoon, 1852

14 Sunday

Railroad engineer Casey Jones born, 1864
Albert Einstein born, 1879
First American bird refuge created at Pelican Island, Florida, 1903

March

Diary

St. Patrick's Day

Wednesday March 17   Today's weather

A Poem about a Shamrock

Lift up your Voices in Praise of Erin's Shore. Where the dear old Shamrock grows For evermore.

Words That Rhyme with "St. Pat"

Words That Rhyme with "Green"

If we should find a pot o' gold,
Hidden at the rainbow's end, o'er yon,
Protected by some droll wee leprechaun,
Here's what we hope that it would hold.

A Memento of Our Day

March

Sun	Mon	Tue	Wed	Thu	Fri	Sat
		1	2	3	4	5	6
7	8	9	10	11	12	13
14	15	16	17	18	19	20
21	22	23	24	25	26	27
28	29	30	31			

Appointments

15 Monday

Ides of March
President Andrew Jackson born, 1767
Maine became the 23rd state, 1820

16 Tuesday

President James Madison born, 1751
First Black newspaper, "Freedom's Journal," published in N.Y.C., 1827

17 Wednesday

St. Patrick's Day
Camp Fire Girls opened to public membership, 1912

18 Thursday

Statesman John Calhoun born, 1782
President Grover Cleveland born, 1837

19 Friday

Massachusetts Bay Colony founded, 1628
Chief Justice Earl Warren born, 1891

20 Saturday

Vernal Equinox: Spring begins at 5:56 p.m. EST

21 Sunday

Entrepeneur Florenz Ziegfeld born, 1869
Hatfield-McCoy feud ends in a marriage, 1891

Returning Birds

Since 1966 when the citizens decided to deliberately attract the birds to eat the town's ever-increasing flying insect pests, purple martins have been arriving in Griggsville, Illinois on March 21. Each bird is estimated to eat 2000 insects daily! Hundreds of purple martin "apartment houses" stand on poles around town, including a huge one in the middle of the town's square.

This is a busy bird week: on the 19th the buzzards return to Hinkley, Ohio, and the swallows to Capistrano, California!

At the Vernal Equinox, the sun crosses the plane of the equator, and the length of the day and night around the world is the same.

March

Diary

Auricular Arachnids?

Spiders ". . . are a very interesting tribe of insects, in spite of their ugly appearance, and the general dislike which most persons, especially females, attach to them, in common with earwigs and other unsightly insects. Naturalists have found out this curious propensity in spiders, that they seem remarkably fond of music, and have been known to descend from the ceiling during concerts, and to retire when the strain was finished."

From The Every-Day Book by William Hone, 1830

"A man cannot do good nor evil to others without doing good or evil to himself."

Uncle Esek, Scribner's Monthly, September 1880

March
Sun Mon Tue Wed Thu Fri Sat
1 2 3 4 5 6
7 8 9 10 11 12 13
14 15 16 17 18 19 20
21 22 23 24 25 26 27
28 29 30 31

Appointments

22 Monday

First Indian Treaty signed, at Plymouth Colony, 1621
Young Men's Hebrew Association founded, N.Y.C., 1874

23 Tuesday

Patrick Henry's "Give me liberty, or give me death" speech made, 1775
Cookbook author Fannie Farmer born, 1857

24 Wednesday

Financier Andrew W. Mellon born, 1855
Magician Harry Houdini born, 1874

25 Thursday

Conductor Arturo Toscanini born, 1867

26 Friday

Poet Robert Frost born, 1874

27 Saturday

Printmaker Nathaniel Currier born, 1813
Photographer Edward Steichen born, 1879

28 Sunday

Band leader Paul Whiteman born, 1891

March

"Like an elephant's trunk, the Grand Jury is strong enough to attack one of the pillars of the temple, and delicate enough to pick up a pin."

From The New York Times, *December 29, 1881*

Diary

April

Sun	Mon	Tue	Wed	Thu	Fri	Sat
				1	2	3
4	5	6	7	8	9	10
11	12	13	14	15	16	17
18	19	20	21	22	23	24
25	26	27	28	29	30	

Fore Runner of the Pony Express

"A newspaper of January 8, mentions an extraordinary feat by Mr. Huddy, the postmaster of Lismore [England], in the 97th year of his age. He travelled, for a wager, from that town to Fermoy in a Dungarvon oyster-tub, drawn by a pig, a badger, two cats, a goose, and a hedgehog; with a large red nightcap on his head, a pig-driver's whip in one hand, and in the other a common cow's horn, which he blew to encourage his team, and give notice of this new mode of posting."

This event of 1821 was reported in The Every-Day Book *by William Hone, 1830*

. . .

I live for those who love me,
  Whose hearts are kind and true,
For heaven that smiles above me,
  And waits my spirit too;
For the cause that lacks assistance,
For the wrong that needs resistance,
For the future in the distance,
  And the good that I can do.

George Linnaeus Banks

Appointments
29 Monday
President John Tyler born, 1790
30 Tuesday
Seward's Day in Alaska—Alaska bought from Russia, 1869 *Doctors' Day, first celebrated 1933*
31 Wednesday
Commodore Perry made "Open Door" treaty with Japan, 1854
1 Thursday
April Fool's Day *Actor Lon Chaney born, 1883*
2 Friday
International Children's Book Day—Hans Christian Andersen born, 1805
3 Saturday
Author Washington Irving born, 1783 *Naturalist John Burroughs born, 1837* *Pony Express began service, Sacramento to St. Louis, 1860*
4 Sunday
Palm Sunday *Ballroom dancer Arthur Murray born, 1895*

$\mathcal{M}$arch $\mathcal{A}$pril

Diary

A Happy Easter

Easter

Sunday April 11

Today's weather

⁓ A Prayer of Hope ⁓

A Memento of Our Day

Write a song for Easter

Menu

Appetizers & Soup

Main Course

Desserts

Bumbershoot or Genes?

"It is the umbrella which has given English men their peculiarly English characteristics. It is obvious that when a man has one hand occupied with an umbrella he is not in a condition to engage in street brawls, for the umbrella is useless as a weapon, and cannot be laid aside in a crowded street without being stolen. It is also to the umbrella that the Englishman owes his characteristic love of respectability. The man who carries an umbrella impliedly proclaims that he wears clothes which would be injured by rain, and that he does not intend to engage in any rash or turbulent adventure. The eminent medical man who made these observations obtained a boy of pure American parentage and began with him a course of umbrella training. The boy was made to keep an umbrella in his hand every moment of his waking hours, and to sleep with it tied to his wrist. Within six months the boy developed a love of Bass's pale ale, a tendency to speak about his bath-tub to every one he met, and had a marked difficulty in the use of the letter 'h.' He has so far failed to show any longing for checked clothing."

From The New York Times, January 3, 1882

•   •   •

As far back as the 1730s there were umbrellas—very rare—in the American colonies. For some reason, for surely umbrellas aren't proscribed in the Bible, there was much religious opposition to umbrellas, especially among the Quakers.

The theme of 1982's World Health Day is "Add life to years" in salute to the elderly.

April						
Sun	Mon	Tue	Wed	Thu	Fri	Sat
				1	2	3
4	5	6	7	8	9	10
11	12	13	14	15	16	17
18	19	20	21	22	23	24
25	26	27	28	29	30	

Appointments

5 Monday

Yale University benefactor Elihu Yale born, 1649
Educator Booker T. Washington born, 1856

6 Tuesday

Mormon Church formally organized, 1830
North Pole reached by Commander Robert E. Peary, 1909

7 Wednesday

World Health Day—World Health Organization established, 1948

8 Thursday

Maunday Thursday
Passover begins
Buddha Day in Hawaii

9 Friday

Good Friday
British statesman Winston Churchill made honorary U.S. citizen, 1963

10 Saturday

Holy Saturday
Salvation Army founder William Booth born, 1829

11 Sunday

Easter

$\mathcal{A}$pril

Diary

April

Sun	Mon	Tue	Wed	Thu	Fri	Sat
				1	2	3
4	5	6	7	8	9	10
11	12	13	14	15	16	17
18	19	20	21	22	23	24
25	26	27	28	29	30	

A Flying Machine

"We must admit that a bird is an incomparable model of a flying machine. No machine that we may hope to devise is half so effective. And yet this machine, thus perfected through infinite ages by a ruthless process of natural selection, reaches its limit of weight at about 50 pounds. Here is another prodigious advantage of the natural, over the artificial, machine. The flying animal is its own engineer. The flying machine must carry its engineer. The directing engineer in the former (brain) is perhaps an ounce; in the latter it is 150 pounds. The limit of the flying animal is 50 pounds.

"The smallest possible weight of a flying machine, with its necessary fuel and engineer, even without freight or passenger, could not be less than 300 or 400 pounds. . . . Is it not demonstrated that a true flying machine, self-raising, self-sustaining, self-propelling, is physically impossible?"

From Popular Science Monthly, *as quoted in* The New-York News-Letter, *January-February 1890*

Footnote: *In June 1981, an announcement was made by an inventor of his new 150-pound "airplane" soon to be marketed to the public!*

"Man is not the only animal that talks. Monkeys chatter and signal to each other, crows caw, bees direct each other to new sources of food by intricate dances. But man is the only animal who can talk from one century or millenium to another. And we do it through books and libraries."

Robert D. Franklin, *in the* Toledo Public Library Annual Report, *1959*

Appointments

12 Monday

Canadian Easter Monday
Statesman Henry Clay born, 1777

13 Tuesday

President Thomas Jefferson born, 1743

14 Wednesday

"S.S. Titanic" struck iceberg, 1912

15 Thursday

Income Tax deadline
Author Henry James born, 1843

16 Friday

Arbor Day in many states
Pioneer of flight Wilbur Wright born, 1867

17 Saturday

Playwright Thornton Wilder born, 1897
American Academy of Arts and Letters founded, 1898

18 Sunday

National Library Week begins
Paul Revere made his famous midnight ride, 1775

April

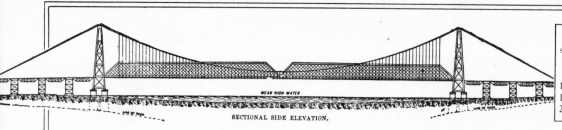

SECTIONAL SIDE ELEVATION.

NEAR HIGH WATER

April

Sun	Mon	Tue	Wed	Thu	Fri	Sat
				1	2	3
4	5	6	7	8	9	10
11	12	13	14	15	16	17
18	19	20	21	22	23	24
25	26	27	28	29	30	

How the Suspension Bride Was Begun

The first suspension bridge at Niagara Falls "was built by Mr. Charles Ellet in 1848. He offered a reward of five dollars to any person who would get a string across the chasm. The next windy day all the boys in the neighborhood were kite-flying; and, before night, a lucky youth landed his kite on the opposite shore and secured the reward. Of this little string was born the large cables which support the present vast structure. But the first *iron* successor of the string was a small wire rope, seven-eights of an inch in diameter. To this was suspended a wire basket, in which two persons could cross the chasm. To it was attached an endless rope that was worked by a windlass on each bank. The ride down to the center was rapid and exhilarating, but the pause over the center, while the slack of the rope was being taken up, was apt to make the coolest person a little nervous, and the *jerky* motion up the opposite slope was rather annoying."

From Scribner's Monthly, August 1876

Appointments

19 Monday

Patriots Day
American Revolutionary War began, 1775

20 Tuesday

Comedian Harold Lloyd born, 1894

21 Wednesday

First bustle patent in America awarded, 1857
Spanish American War began, 1898

22 Thursday

"In God We Trust" first appeared on U.S. coins, on a 2¢ piece, 1864
Earth Day first celebrated, 1970

23 Friday

William Shakespeare born, 1565
President James Buchanan born, 1791

24 Saturday

Library of Congress established, 1800

25 Sunday

Daylight Saving begins—set your clocks ahead
Singer Ella Fitzgerald born, 1918

April

Diary

April

Sun	Mon	Tue	Wed	Thu	Fri	Sat
				1	2	3
4	5	6	7	8	9	10
11	12	13	14	15	16	17
18	19	20	21	22	23	24
25	26	27	28	29	30	

Lessons in Telegraphy

A.—   A dot and a dash is A,

B—...   A dash and three dots B,

C.. .   Two dots, a space, and one dot C,

D—..   A dash and two dots D.

E.   One single dot for E.

F.—.   For F a dot, dash, dot,

G— —.   Two dashes and a dot for G.

H....   H, four dots you'll allot.

I..   Two dots will stand for I.

J—.—.   A dash, dot, dash, dot, J.

K—.—   For K, a dash, dot, dash, you try

L———   A long dash L away.

M— —   Two dashes M demands.

N—.   A dash and a dot for N.

O. .   A dot, a space, and dot, O stands.

P.....   Five dots for P, not ten.

Q..—.   Two dots, dash, dot, are q.

R. ..   A dot, space, two dots, R.

S...   For S, three dots will always do.

T—   One dash is T, thus far.

U..—   Two dots, a dash, for U.

V...—   Three dots a dash for V.

W.— —   Dot, two dashes, W.

X.—..   Dot, dash, two dots, X see.

Y.. ..   Two dots, space, two dots, Y.

Z... .   Three dots, space, dot, are Z.

&. ...   A dot, space, three dots, & decry.

Period..— —..   A period is U D.

From The Chatterbox, September 1881

"Even the tiniest spider can cause bridges to
be built, live in the castle of his choosing
and sleep surrounded by silk."
Grace McFarland

Appointments

26 Monday

Confederate Memorial Day
Nature artist John James Audubon born, 1785
Urban landscape architect, Frederick Law Olmsted born, 1822

27 Tuesday

Inventor, painter & telegraphist Samuel F. B. Morse born, 1791
President Ulysses S. Grant born, 1822

28 Wednesday

President James Monroe born, 1758
Maryland became the 7th state, 1788
Actor Lionel Barrymore born, 1878

29 Thursday

Newspaper magnate William Randolph Hearst born, 1863
Jazz great Duke Ellington born, 1899

30 Friday

Arbor Day in many states
Louisiana became the 18th state, 1812

1 Saturday

May Day, Law Day & Hawaiian Lei Day
Kentucky Derby, Louisville
First U. S. postal card issued, 1873

2 Sunday

Be Kind to Animals Week begins
Singer Bing Crosby born, 1904

$\mathcal{A}$pril $\mathcal{M}$ay

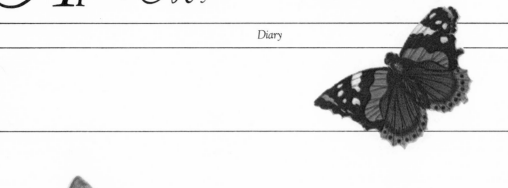

A World's Fair, with energy as its theme, opens in downtown Knoxville, Tennessee on May 1, and runs through October 31.

Diary

Mother's Day

Sunday May 9

Today's weather

A Memento of Our Day

A Picture of Mother

Circle The Menu
for Mother's Day

Peas*Corn*Souffle*Chicken*Broccoli*
Strawberries*Pineapple*Beans*Kale*
Fried Apples*Hotdogs*Meatloaf*BLTs*
Waldorf Salad*Baked Beans*Chocolate
Cake*Brussel Sprouts*Onion Rings*
Bluefish*Tuna Salad*Celery Sticks*
Tomato Soup*Ripe Olives*Pork Lo
Mein*Clam Sauce Spaghetti*Carrots*
Beets*Banana Bread*Scrambled Eggs*

MOM • MUMMY • MA • MAMMY • MAMA • MOTHER . . .

We call our mother everything but "Pop"!

_____calls her "_____,"

_____calls her "_____,".

_____calls her "_____,"

_____calls her "_____,"

_____calls her "_____,"

_____calls her "_____,"

_____calls her "_____,"

and she calls herself "_____."

51

May

Sun Mon Tue Wed Thu Fri Sat
1
2 3 4 5 6 7 8
9 10 11 12 13 14 15
16 17 18 19 20 21 22
23/30 24/31 25 26 27 28 29

May is building her house. With apple
    blooms she is roofing over the
    glimmering rooms;
Of the oak and the beech hath she builded
    its beams, and, spinning all
    day at her secret looms,
With arras of leaves each wind-swayed wall
She pictureth over, and peopleth it all
    with echoes and dreams,
    And singing of streams.

May is building her house. Of
    petal and blade,
Of the roots of the oak, is the
    flooring made,
    With a carpet of mosses and lichen
    and clover, each small miracle
    over and over,
And tender, traveling green things
    strayed.

                        ...

Richard Le Gallienne

Appointments

3 Monday

First medical school in U.S. founded at College of Philadelphia, 1765
Friends of Animals founded, 1957

4 Tuesday

Diary Look-alike Contest Deadline
Educator Horace Mann born, 1796

5 Wednesday

Journalist Nelly Bly born, 1867
Author Christopher Morley born, 1890

6 Thursday

World's first postage stamp, "penny black," issued in Great Britain, 1840
Civil Rights Act passed by House & Senate, 1960

7 Friday

The American Veterinary Association formed in Philadelphia, 1854
Poet Archibald MacLeish born, 1892

8 Saturday

Native American Day
President Harry S Truman born, 1884

9 Sunday

Mother's Day
Abolitionist John Brown born, 1800

May

Diary

Look-alike No. 2

May

Sun	Mon	Tue	Wed	Thu	Fri	Sat
						1
2	3	4	5	6	7	8
9	10	11	12	13	14	15
16	17	18	19	20	21	22
23/30 24/31	25	26	27	28	29	

The Arrow and the Song

I shot an arrow into the air,
It fell to earth, I knew not where;
For, so swiftly it flew, the sight
Could not follow it in its flight.

I breathed a song into the air,
It fell to earth, I knew not where;
For who has sight so keen and strong,
That it can follow the flight of song?

Long, long afterward, in an oak
I found the arrow, still unbroke;
And the song, from beginning to end,
I found again in the heart of a friend.

Henry Wadsworth Longfellow

"Don't forget this, my boy: there are ten
thousand ways to miss the bull's-eye, and
only one way to hit it."

Uncle Esek, Century Magazine, 1885

Appointments

10 Monday

Union Pacific and Central Pacific Railroads joined, 1869
Dancer Fred Astaire born, 1899

11 Tuesday

Minnesota became the 32nd state, 1858

12 Wednesday

English nurse Florence Nightingale born, 1820

13 Thursday

First permanent American settlement, Jamestown, Virginia, 1607

14 Friday

Lewis & Clark left to explore the Northeast Territory, 1804
First Olympic games held in U.S., 1904

15 Saturday

Preakness Stakes, Pimlico, Maryland
First regular airmail service began, 1918

16 Sunday

Rogation Sunday
Entertainer Liberace born, 1919

May

Diary

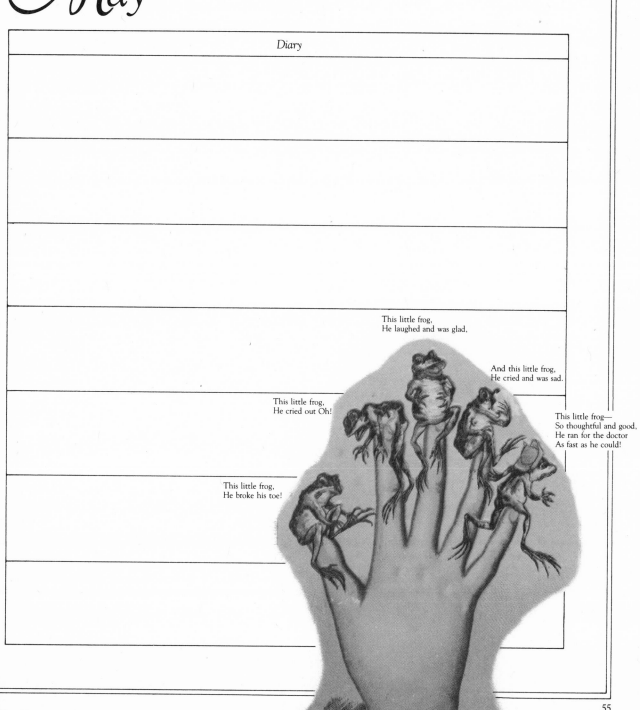

This little frog,
He laughed and was glad,

And this little frog,
He cried and was sad.

This little frog,
He cried out Oh!

This little frog—
So thoughtful and good,
He ran for the doctor
As fast as he could!

This little frog,
He broke his toe!

Titania's Pen

A humming-bird had plumed his wing
  With nice fastidious bill,
And Oberon, the fairy king,
  Picked up a fallen quill.

Quoth he, "Of this I'll make a pen,
  The neatest ever seen."
He trimmed the tiny quill, and then
  He gave it to his queen.

The fair Titania wrote a book
  With this same elfin quill;
The dainty pen—I have it, look!
  The book I search for still.

Perhaps 't is hid among the ferns,
  Or in some squirrel's cell,
Or from its leaves the young bird learns
  In easy notes to spell.

Edith M. Thomas, 1895

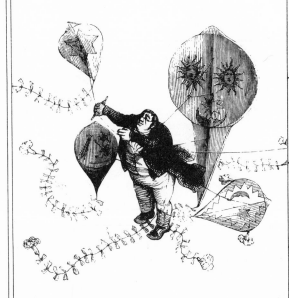

. . . *And the Vacca Jumped over the Lunae*
Hei didulum! atque iterum didulum!
Felisque fidesque, vacca super lunae cornua
  prosiluit:
Nescio qua catulus riset dulcedine ludi;
Abstulit et turpi cochleare fuga.

From Margaret by Sylvester Judd, 1845

May

Sun	Mon	Tue	Wed	Thu	Fri	Sat
						1
2	3	4	5	6	7	8
9	10	11	12	13	14	15
16	17	18	19	20	21	22
23/30 24/31	25	26	27	28	29	

Appointments

17 Monday

Armed Forces Day
First Kentucky Derby held, 1875

18 Tuesday

Panama Canal opened to barge service, 1914

19 Wednesday

Philanthropist Johns Hopkins born, 1795

20 Thursday

Ascension Day
Lindbergh flew the Atlantic, 1927
Amelia Earhart Putnam makes first solo woman's flight over Atlantic, 1932

21 Friday

American Red Cross founded, 1881

22 Saturday

National Maritime Day

23 Sunday

South Carolina became the 8th state, 1788
Daylight Saving was the issue on first radio debate, Washington D.C., 1922

May

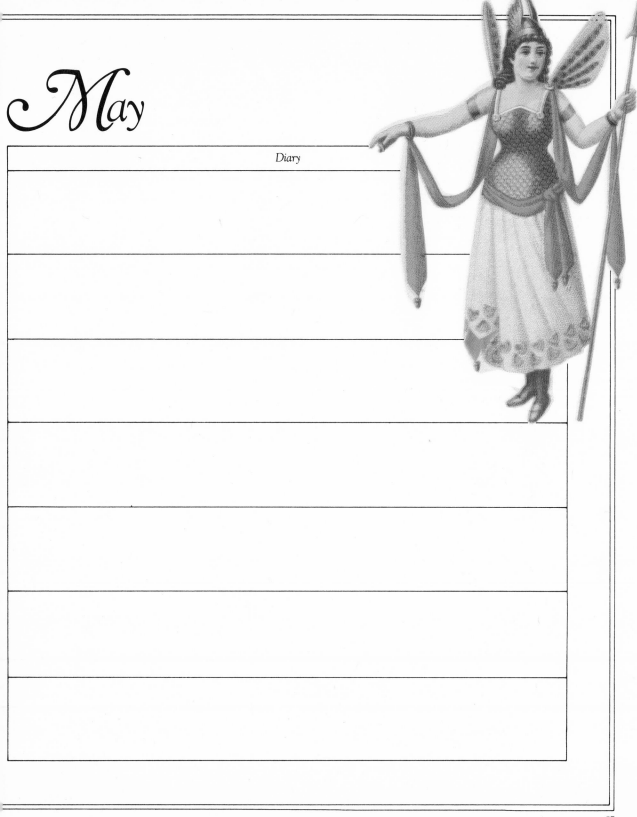

Diary

Saving Baby Birds

A fully feathered baby bird, which hops but can't fly, is best put in a protected tree or bush close to the spot where found. The parents *will* return. Babies found in city streets, or unprotected areas, may be cared for, with frequent success, by feeding every half hour a mixture of ¼ cup dry dog food, 1 chopped hardboiled egg *yolk*, 1 tsp. wheat germ, ⅛ tsp. garden soil, and water. Use blunt toothpick to push food far down throat—baby will help by holding beak wide open. Feed about a half-a- thimble-full each time. Keep bird in tissue-lined strawberry box nest, 95° to 100°F. Water may be touched to tip of beak; never force with eyedropper. After a week or so, transfer to larger carton, with screening top, and natural branch perches. When feathers of tail and wing are long enough for flight, release bird in protected spot. For further reading: *Bird Ambulance* and other books by Arline Thomas.

Ho! I'm going back to where
We were youngsters.—Meet me there,
Dear old barefoot chum, and we
Will be as we used to be,—
Lawless rangers up and down
The old creek beyond the town—

...

From Our Boyhood Haunts by James Whitcomb Riley

May						
Sun	Mon	Tue	Wed	Thu	Fri	Sat
						1
2	3	4	5	6	7	8
9	10	11	12	13	14	15
16	17	18	19	20	21	22
23/30	24/31	25	26	27	28	29

Appointments

24 Monday

Victoria Day in Canada
Brooklyn Bridge opened, 1883

25 Tuesday

Poet Ralph Waldo Emerson born, 1803
Boxer Gene Tunney born, 1898

26 Wednesday

Actor Al Jolson born, 1886

27 Thursday

Environmentalist Rachel Carson born, 1907
San Francisco's Golden Gate Bridge opened, 1937

28 Friday

Shavuoth
Dionne Quintuplets born in Quebec, 1934

29 Saturday

Rhode Island became the 13th state, 1790; Wisconsin became the 30th, 1848
President John F. Kennedy born, 1917

30 Sunday

Whit Sunday or Pentecost
Memorial Day traditionally observed

May

Diary

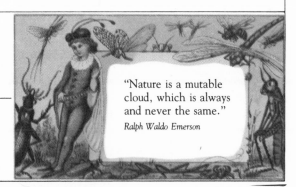

"Nature is a mutable cloud, which is always and never the same."

Ralph Waldo Emerson

Memorial Day

Today's weather

We celebrated on May _____

A Memento of Our Day

The Names of Those
We Wish to Remember Today

We Spent Memorial Day This Way

Write a Prayer for Love, Peace & Memory

EXTRA! EXTRA!
THE HOME NEWS
THIS YEAR   TODAY   ONE CENT
HELP! I'm simply dying for
news from home! And all the
folks I love so dearly. To hear
all the gossip that's going 'round.
So please write soon and
oblige — Yours Sincerely.

June

Sun	Mon	Tue	Wed	Thu	Fri	Sat
	1	2	3	4	5	
6	7	8	9	10	11	12
13	14	15	16	17	18	19
20	21	22	23	24	25	26
27	28	29	30			

Hurricane Names by Ocean

Since 1978, men's names have been included in the hurricane name lists prepared by the National Hurricane Center near Miami. The 1982 names will be used again in 1988.

ATLANTIC		EASTERN NORTH PACIFIC	
Alberto	Leslie	Aletta	Lane
Beryl	Michael	Bud	Miriam
Chris	Nadine	Carlotta	Norman
Debby	Oscar	Daniel	Olivia
Ernesto	Patty	Emilia	Paul
Florence	Rafael	Fabio	Rosa
Gilbert	Sandy	Gilma	Sergio
Helene	Tony	Hector	Tara
Issac	Valerie	Iva	Vicente
Joan	William	John	Willa
Keith		Kristy	

"Hello There! Hi! Hi! Hello!"

Hoover, a 230-pound harbor seal at the New England Aquarium on the Boston Harbor waterfront has taught himself English in only four years! In response to the greetings offered by men, women and children who come to the aquarium, Hoover salutes his visitors with his own deep-voiced, clear *Hello, Hello there, Hi* and *Hoover*—all of which he embellishes with gusts of hearty chuckles. A younger seal named Salisbury (found on Salisbury Beach) is an up-and-coming linguist too—he learned "Hello!" from harbor seal trainer Jacquie Buehler, but added a "there" probably because of Hoover.

Hoover, who has lived most of his life in the harbor seal pool—surrounded by strandlings of various ages, is the father of two. His own birthday is celebrated on June 2, and he will be 11 in 1982. The aquarium is on Central Wharf, and the harbor seal pool is at the entrance, if you want to say "Hello! Hello there! Hi! Hi! Happy Birthday, Hoover!"

Appointments

31 Monday

Memorial Day, legal holiday
Poet Walt Whitman born, 1819

1 Tuesday

Adopt-a-Cat Month in U.S. & Canada
Hurricane Season from now till 11/30
Kentucky became the 15th state, 1792; Tennessee the 16th, 1796

2 Wednesday

Tarzan Johnny Weissmuller born, 1904
Harbor seal Hoover born, 1971

3 Thursday

Gemini 4 astronaut Ed White "walked" in space, 1965

4 Friday

Anniversary of Jack Jouett's Ride in Virginia, 1784

5 Saturday

Belmont Stakes, New York
World Environment Day

6 Sunday

Pat a Cat Day
Patriot Nathan Hale born, 1755

May June

Diary

Look-alike No. 3

June

Sun Mon Tue Wed Thu Fri Sat
                 1 2 3 4 5
 6 7 8 9 10 11 12
13 14 15 16 17 18 19
20 21 22 23 24 25 26
27 28 29 30

The Indian moccason, or lady's slipper "... is to me especially suggestive of the wilder woods. When we find its striped pink pouch swinging from a stout stem between two large veiny leaves, it looks as though it were guarding some mysterious secret. It was almost a disappointment last year to come across a whole flock of these flowers beneath the pines which skirted a neighbor's lawn. When an orchid leaves its exclusive haunts for a gentleman's country seat we feel a little as if a queen had stepped from her throne to mingle promiscuously with her subjects."

From According to Season
by Mrs. William Starr Dana, 1894

"One reason why we all grow wise so slowly, is because we nurse our mistakes too fondly."

Uncle Esek, Scribner's Monthly, September 1880

Appointments

7 Monday

Boone Day—Daniel Boone first saw Kentucky, 1769

8 Tuesday

Ice cream first advertised, 1786
Architect Frank Lloyd Wright born, 1867

9 Wednesday

Song writer Cole Porter born, 1893

10 Thursday

Singer & actress Judy Garland born, 1922
Alcoholics Anonymous founded, 1935

11 Friday

King Kamehameha Day in Hawaii—celebrating uniting of the islands

12 Saturday

Abner Doubleday invented baseball at Cooperstown, N.Y., 1839
Vice-President George Bush born, 1924

13 Sunday

Children's Day
Yukon Territory organized, 1898

June

Diary

Sunday June 20

Father's Day

Today's weather

A Memento of Our Day

POP • DADDY • PAPPY • PA • FATHER

We call our father everything but late to dinner!

_____ *calls him* " _____ ,"

_____ *calls him* " _____ ,"

_____ *calls him* " _____ ,"

_____ *calls him* " _____ ,"

_____ *calls him* " _____ ,"

_____ *calls him* " _____ ,"

_____ *calls him* " _____ ,"

and he calls himself " _____ ,"

Father Knows Best

When it comes to:

The Menu on Father's Day

Who fixed the meal?

A Song for Father

Sung to the tune of

June

Sun Mon Tue Wed Thu Fri Sat
1 2 3 4 5
6 7 8 9 10 11 12
13 14 15 16 17 18 19
20 21 22 23 24 25 26
27 28 29 30

Appointments

14 Monday

Flag Day in most states
Balladist Burl Ives born, 1909

15 Tuesday

Ben Franklin flew his kite in a lightning storm, 1752
Arkansas became the 25th state, 1836

16 Wednesday

Alaska Gold Rush began, 1897

17 Thursday

Battle of Bunker Hill, 1775

18 Friday

Susan B. Anthony arrested for voting,
refused to pay fine and was released, 1872

19 Saturday

Slaves in Texas declared free, 1865
Baseball great Lou Gehrig born, 1903

20 Sunday

Father's Day—first observed 1910
Midsummer's Day celebrated in Alaska
West Virginia became the 35th state, 1863

There's a Bower of Bean-Vines

There's a bower of bean-vines
   in Benjamin's yard,
  And the cabbages grow round it,
   planted for greens;
In the time of my childhood
   'twas terribly hard
To bend down the bean-poles,
   and pick off the beans.

That bower and its products
   I never forget,
  But oft, when my landlady
   presses me hard,
I think, are the cabbages
   growing there yet,
  Are the bean-vines still bearing
   in Benjamin's yard?

No, the bean-vines soon withered
   that once used to wave,
  But some beans had been gathered,
   the last that hung on;
And a soup was distilled in a kettle,
   that gave
All the fragrance of summer
   when summer was gone.

Thus memory draws from delight,
   ere it dies,
  An essence that breathes of it
   awfully hard;
As thus good to my taste
   as 'twas then to my eyes,
  Is that bower of bean-vines
   in Benjamin's yard.

Phoebe Cary

June

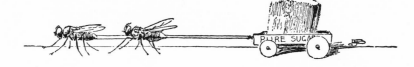

Diary

The Ballade of the Coming Rain

When the morning swoons in its highest heat,
  And the sunshine dims, and no dark shade
Streaks the dust of the dazzling street,
  And the long straw splits in the lemonade;
  When the cirucus lags in a sad parade,
And the drum throbs dull as a pulse of pain,
  And the breezeless flags hang limp and frayed—
O then is the time to look for rain.

When the man on the watering cart bumps by,
  Trilling the air of an old fife-tune,
With a dull, soiled smile, and one shut eye,
  Lost in a dream of the afternoon;
  When the awning sags like a lank balloon,
And a thick sweat stands on the windowpane,
  And a five-cent fan is a priceless boon—
O then is the time to look for rain.

...

James Whitcomb Riley, 1900

...
In summer's even,
There hop, between the *blades* of Heaven
  And hailstones pearly droppers,
Insects of mirth, whose songs so shrill
Delight the *ears* of vale and hill,
  The grassy, green—GRASS-HOPPERS.

J.R.P., 1827

June
Sun Mon Tue Wed Thu Fri Sat
. 1 2 3 4 5
6 7 8 9 10 11 12
13 14 15 16 17 18 19
20 21 22 23 24 25 26
27 28 29 30

Appointments
21 Monday
Summer Solstice: summer begins 1:23 p.m. DST
New Hampshire became the 9th state, 1788
22 Tuesday
Author Anne Morrow Lindberg born, 1906
23 Wednesday
William Penn signed treaty with Indians, 1683
William Sholes patented his typewriter, 1868
24 Thursday
Fête Nationale in Quebec
Preacher Henry Ward Beecher born, 1813
25 Friday
Virginia became the 10th state, 1788
26 Saturday
United Nations charter signed by 50 countries, 1945
27 Sunday
"Air conditioning" first installed in a theatre, 1848
Helen Keller born, 1880

June

Diary

Fourth of July

Today's weather

Main Street, Ellsworth, Me.

We Spend Independence Day This Way

Our Family Treasures These Freedoms

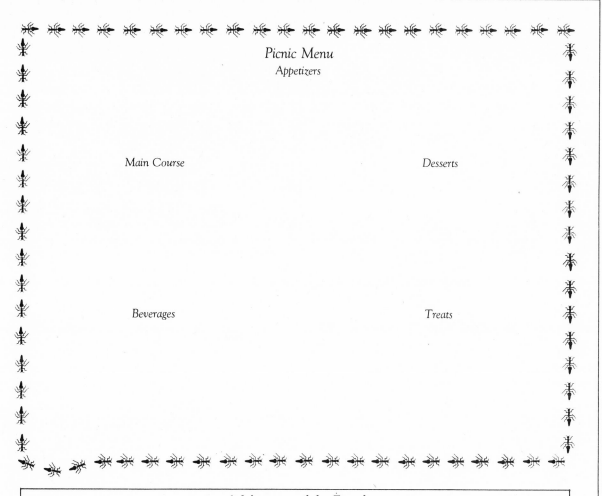

Picnic Menu

Appetizers

Main Course

Desserts

Beverages

Treats

A Memento of the Fourth

A Summer Evening in Florida
Circa 1837

"Sunset was announced by a general uproar
in the yard. . . . Then came the reign of
the musquitoes . . . [that] rose in the air
like a cloud, filling the ears with their
unwelcome piping hum, the face and hands
with blisters, and the heart with spite and
impatience. The Florida musquito is the
redoubted 'gallinipper' of the South; and a
dozen stings are sufficient to make you sore
for a week. The dragon-flies which are large
and numerous, and voracious, are now seen
flitting among them, and destroying
thousands, but what are thousands, when
the very motes of the atmosphere seem
turned into myriads?"

From The Crockett Almanacks, *originally published in*
Nashville, 1835 to 1838

"There are lots of things in this world we
can't explain, and that is just what makes
the things we can explain the more
certain."

Uncle Esek, Century Magazine, *1885*

Fair insect! that, with thread-like
   legs spread out,
  And blood-extracting bill,
   and filmy wing,
Dost murmur, as thou
   slowly sail'st about,
  In pitiless ears,
   fall many a plaintive thing,
And tell how little
   our large veins should bleed
Would we but yield them
   to thy bitter need.

     ...

From "The Mosquito" by William Cullen Bryant

July

Sun	Mon	Tue	Wed	Thu	Fri	Sat
				1	2	3
4	5	6	7	8	9	10
11	12	13	14	15	16	17
18	19	20	21	22	23	24
25	26	27	28	29	30	31

Appointments

28 Monday

Versailles Treaty ending WWI signed, 1919

29 Tuesday

Crooner Nelson Eddy born, 1901

30 Wednesday

Singer Lena Horne born, 1917

1 Thursday

Dominion Day in Canada
President Lincoln signed bill subsidizing
railroad and creating transcontinental line, 1862

2 Friday

Justice Thurgood Marshall born, 1908

3 Saturday

Beginning of "Dog Days"
Idaho became the 43rd state, 1890
Veterans' Administration created, 1930

4 Sunday

Independence Day—Declaration of Independence adopted, 1776

June *July*

Diary

"Strive not with a man without cause, if he have done thee no harm."
Proverbs 3:30

July

Sun	Mon	Tue	Wed	Thu	Fri	Sat
				1	2	3
4	5	6	7	8	9	10
11	12	13	14	15	16	17
18	19	20	21	22	23	24
25	26	27	28	29	30	31

HAD FORGOTTEN SOMETHING

From the Americus (Ga.) Republican

"A rather young-looking gentleman, living near the Marion County line, brought his family to the city on the day that the circus was here to let them see the animals. After seeing all the sights, the show, the horses, dogs, and clown, he gathered his family and started home. When he had gone a mile he turned to his wife and remarked, "I feel just like I've left something. She replied, "If you feel that way then you have," so they stopped and made their children file before them as they called the roll. One of the youngsters came up missing, so they returned to the city and found their little boy sitting at Carter's shoe store waiting patiently until his father would carry the others home and return for him. There was great joy in that family on the recovery of the lost boy. This is true."

From The New York Times, *December 27, 1881*

Appointments

5 Monday

Circus entrepeneur Phineas T. Barnum born, 1810
Salvation Army founded in London, 1865

6 Tuesday

"Lights of New York," first all-talkie movie, shown, 1928

7 Wednesday

Hawaii annexed by the U.S., 1898

8 Thursday

Financier John D. Rockefeller born, 1839
Governor of N.Y. Nelson Rockefeller born, 1908

9 Friday

National Fast Day inaugurated, 1832
Inventor of the sewing machine, Elias Howe, born, 1819

10 Saturday

Artist James McNeill Whistler born, 1834
Wyoming became the 44th state, 1890

11 Sunday

President John Quincy Adams born, 1767

July

Diary

MARY AND HER LITTLE BEAR BEHIND.

July

Sun	Mon	Tue	Wed	Thu	Fri	Sat
				1	2	3
4	5	6	7	8	9	10
11	12	13	14	15	16	17
18	19	20	21	22	23	24
25	26	27	28	29	30	31

Success

Who wins the race? The boy who strives
For victory solely, and derives
No pleasure from the racer's art,
Nor keen delight to play his part,
But, struggling for his flag or button,
Must bolt his triumph like a glutton?

Who wins the race? The maid who craves
That all her friends should be her slaves?
A warm look here, cold shoulder there,
Now wafting bliss and now despair!
Amid the herd her charms have smitten
Gives on a finger, ten the mitten!

Who wins the race? The man who pours
His every nerve where he adores,
Outstrips his foes at any rate
And gets the maid by efforts great,
So set on owning that he's blind
To hot or cold, to wet or wind?

The race—who wins it? It is he
Who loses, gains the loftier fee!
O boy, love racing, not the prize;
Love love, sweet girl, not lover's cries;
And, man, far sooner bear a hurt
Than stoop to wrangle for a flirt!

Charles de Kay, Scribner's Monthly, June 1880

Appointments

12 Monday

Photography pioneer George Eastman born, 1854
Composer Oscar Hammerstein born, 1895

13 Tuesday

Confederate cavalry commander Nathan Bedford Forrest born, 1821

14 Wednesday

President Gerald R. Ford born, 1913

15 Thursday

St. Swithin's Day

16 Friday

District of Columbia organized, 1790

17 Saturday

Douglas "Wrong way" Corrigan flew on purpose to Dublin instead of L.A. because he couldn't get a visa to Europe, 1938

18 Sunday

First patriotic song, "The Liberty Song," published in "Boston Gazette," 1768

July

Diary

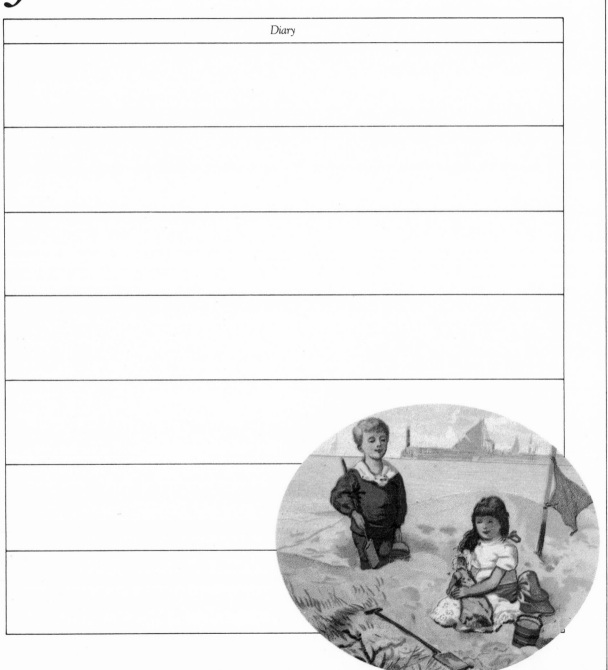

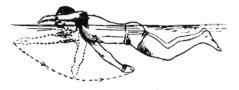

July

Sun	Mon	Tue	Wed	Thu	Fri	Sat
					1	2	3
4	5	6	7	8	9	10
11	12	13	14	15	16	17
18	19	20	21	22	23	24
25	26	27	28	29	30	31

Has it Happened Yet?

"A curious feature of work by women is that, while in this century and in America work and money-earning have always been considered to be proper in every way for men, there is still some slight social stigma pertaining to money-getting by women. This may be trusted to die out as fast as women show that they can retain all the most attractive attributes of womanhood and yet earn their own living."

From The House and Home, 1896

Seven Deadly Sins

Politics without principle.
Wealth without work.
Pleasure without conscience.
Knowledge without character.
Business without morality.
Science without humanity.
Worship without sacrifice.

"Building air-castles is a harmless business as long as you don't attempt to live in them."
Uncle Esek, Scribner's Monthly, September 1880

Appointments
19 Monday
First Woman's Rights Convention, Seneca Falls, N.Y., 1848
20 Tuesday
Astronauts Neil Armstrong & Buzz Aldrin walked on moon, 1969
21 Wednesday
Writer & adventurer Ernest Hemingway born, 1899
22 Thursday
Moses Cleaveland settled on site of Cleveland, Ohio, 1796
23 Friday
First American swimming school opened, in Boston, 1828
First ice cream cone made, 1904
24 Saturday
Aviator Amelia Earhart born, 1898
25 Sunday
Constitution Day in Puerto Rico

July

Diary

July

Sun	Mon	Tue	Wed	Thu	Fri	Sat
					1	2	3
4	5	6	7	8	9	10
11	12	13	14	15	16	17
18	19	20	21	22	23	24
25	26	27	28	29	30	31

Bobolink's Song

"I have noticed that the bobolink does not sing the same in different localities. In New Jersey it has one song; on the Hudson a slight variation of the same, and on the high grass lands of the interior of New York State, quite a different strain,—clearer, more distinctly articulated, and running off with more sparkle and liltingness. It reminds one of the clearer mountain air and the translucent spring-water of those localities. I never could make out what the bobolink says in New Jersey, but in certain districts in New York his enunciation is quite distinct. Sometimes he begins with the word *gegue, gegue.* Then again, more fully, *be true to me, Clarsy, be true to me, Clarsy, Clarsy,* thence full tilt into his inimitable song, interspersed in which the words *kick your slipper, kick your slipper,* and *temperance, temperance* (the last with a peculiar nasal resonance), are plainly heard. At its best, it is a remarkable performance."

John Burroughs, in Scribner's Monthly, *August 1876.*

Appointments

26 Monday

Postal system established in America, 1775
New York became the 11th state, 1788

27 Tuesday

First permanent Atlantic cable completed, 1866
Korean War ended, 1953

28 Wednesday

Annual Pony-Penning Festival, Chincoteague Island, Virginia
Constitutional Amendment XIV,
granting citizenship to Negroes, adopted, 1868

29 Thursday

Author Booth Tarkington born, 1869

30 Friday

Industrialist Henry Ford born, 1863
United States joins UNESCO, 1946

31 Saturday

First patent registered in U.S., awarded to Samuel Hopkins of Vermont
for a potash manufacturing process, 1790

1 Sunday

Author Herman Melville born, 1819
Colorado became the 38th state, 1876

July August

Diary

Obstinance

"Weeds have this virture: they are not easily discouraged; they never lose heart entirely; they die game. If they cannot have the best they will take up with the poorest; if fortune is unkind to them to-day, they hope for better luck to-morrow; if they cannot lord it over a corn-hill, they will sit humbly at its foot and accept what comes; in all cases they make the most of their opportunities."

From "Notes of a Walker" by John Burroughs, in Scribner's Monthly, May 1880

Uncle Sidney's Logic

Pa wunst he scold' an' says to me,—
  "Don't *play* so much, but try
To *study* more, and nen you'll be
  A great man, by an' by."
Nen Uncle Sidney says, "You let
  Him *be* a boy an' play.—
The greatest man on earth, I bet,
  'Ud trade with him today!"

James Whitcomb Riley, 1900

August

Sun	Mon	Tue	Wed	Thu	Fri	Sat
	1	2	3	4	5	6	7
8	9	10	11	12	13	14
15	16	17	18	19	20	21
22	23	24	25	26	27	28
29	30	31				

Appointments

2 Monday

First on-the-street mailbox, Boston, 1858

3 Tuesday

Christopher Columbus sailed from Spain, 1492
In first intercollegiate rowing race, Harvard beat Yale, 1853

4 Wednesday

U.S. Coast Guard Day
Chautauqua Literary & Scientific Circle founded, 1874

5 Thursday

First Federal income tax signed into law, 1861

6 Friday

Comedian Lucille Ball born, 1911
Judge Crater, of the N.Y. State Supreme Court, disappeared, 1930

7 Saturday

United Nations diplomat Ralph Bunche born, 1904

8 Sunday

Poet Sara Teasdale born, 1884

August

The pictures below are composites—prints made by using multiple negatives. The portraits look in a way like everybody in a group and nobody in particular! The man at left is a composite of 22 Doctors of Philosophy from Johns Hopkins University; at right is a composite of 47 female members of the class of '87 at Mount Holyoke! From The Century Illustrated Monthly, *November 1887.*

Diary

Look-alikes No's. 4 & 5

August

Sun	Mon	Tue	Wed	Thu	Fri	Sat
1	2	3	4	5	6	7
8	9	10	11	12	13	14
15	16	17	18	19	20	21
22	23	24	25	26	27	28
29	30	31				

"There is a hollow in the meadow which is always too wet to be explored comfortably without rubber boots, and which becomes at high tide a salt-water pond. Its edges are guarded by ranks of tall swamp mallows, whose great rose-colored flowers flutter like banners in the breeze. Close by are thickets turned pinkish-purple by the dense flower-clusters of the largest and most showy of the tick-trefoils, a group of plants which are now [August] in full bloom, and which can be recognized by their three-divided leaves, pink or purple pea-like flowers, and by the flat, roughened pods, which adhere to our clothes with regrettable pertinacity. The botany assigns this species to rich woods, but I have never seen it more abundant than here."

From According to Season by Mrs. William Starr Dana, 1894

Appointments

9 Monday

Zebulon Pike seeks source of Mississippi River, 1805
First electric washing machine patented, 1901

10 Tuesday

Missouri became the 24th state, 1821
President Herbert Hoover born, 1874

11 Wednesday

Art collector Joseph Hirshhorn born, 1899

12 Thursday

Author Mary Roberts Rinehart born, 1876
Moviemaker Cecil B. De Mille born, 1881

13 Friday

Annie Oakley born, 1860
Suspense movie great Alfred Hitchcock born, 1899

14 Saturday

Social Security Act passed by Congress, 1935

15 Sunday

Actress Ethel Barrymore born, 1879
Television chef & author Julia Child born, 1912

August

Diary

Cartoon © 1908, American Journal Examiner

August

	Sun	Mon	Tue	Wed	Thu	Fri	Sat
		1	2	3	4	5	6	7
	8	9	10	11	12	13	14
	15	16	17	18	19	20	21
	22	23	24	25	26	27	28
	29	30	31				

Born August 1786
Died 1836

"Everything here is Davy Crockett. He was a member of Congress. His voice was so rough it could not be described—it was obliged to be drawn as a picture. He took hailstones for 'Life Pills' when he was unwell—he picked his teeth with a pitchfork—combed his hair with a rake—fanned himself with a hurricane, wore a cast-iron shirt, and drank nothing but creosote and aquafortis. . . . He snored so loud that he was obliged to sleep at a house in the next street for fear of waking himself. He had a farm, which was so rocky, that, when they planted the corn, they were obliged to shoot the grains into the crevices of the rocks with muskets. . . ."

From Echoes from the Backwood by Captain R. G. A. Levinge, London, 1849—an account of his American travels and here, in suitable tall-tale style, a short biography of the legendary Crockett

"The woodsman who is never lost in the woods but who on occasion may not know just where he is, follows two simple rules. First, always go downhill, for this will lead you to water. Then follow the water downstream, for this will always take you, as he phrases it, 'out into the clear.' "

From The Maine Woods by Henry David Thoreau

Appointments

16 Monday

Discovery Day in Yukon Province, Canada
Gold found in Alaska, 1896
First transatlantic cable message sent, 1859

17 Tuesday

Davy Crockett born, 1786
Actress Mae West born, 1893

18 Wednesday

Explorer Meriwether Lewis born, 1774
Citizens of Gloucester, Massachusetts, reported sea serpent off coast, 1818

19 Thursday

Pioneer of flight Orville Wright born, 1871
Humorist Ogden Nash born, 1902

20 Friday

Alaska discovered, 1791
President Benjamin Harrison born, 1833

21 Saturday

Hawaii became the 50th state, 1959

22 Sunday

Poet Dorothy Parker born, 1893

August

Diary

August

Sun	Mon	Tue	Wed	Thu	Fri	Sat
	1	2	3	4	5	6	7
8	9	10	11	12	13	14
15	16	17	18	19	20	21
22	23	24	25	26	27	28
29	30	31				

A Back-Handed Speller

"Santa Fe has a young man with a mind which has a faculty that is rarely to be found, if indeed it can ever be discovered elsewhere. The gentleman is Hugh McKevitt, a printer at Military Headquarters. McKevitt defies anyone to put at him a word which he cannot spell backward as rapidly as the best and quickest speller could give it the usual way.

"The other day this reporter tested McKevitt. As soon as the first word was pronounced, Mc said 'Fifteen letters' and went at it backward so fast that his hearers were unable to tell whether he was right or wrong. The strangest part about the whole thing is that McKevitt has never practised or studied spelling backward a day in his life. He says as soon as he hears a word he knows how many letters are in it and how to spell it backward or forward. It is so, too, with sentences.

"There is no particular advantage in all this as far as can be discovered, but it is a curiosity and a rare one, and if anybody thinks it isn't hard to do let him try to acquire it."

From The New York Times, *December 25, 1881*

Limerick of the
Simplified Spelling Society

A merchant addressing a debtor
Remarked in the course of his lebtor
That he chose to suppose
A man knose what he ose
And the sooner he pays it the bebtor!

Appointments

23 Monday

Dancer Gene Kelly born, 1912

24 Tuesday

President Lincoln received first coast-to-coast telegram, from Sacramento, 1861
Amelia Earhart made non-stop transcontinental flight, 1932

25 Wednesday

City of New Orleans founded, 1718
National Park Service established, 1916

26 Thursday

Constitutional Amendment XIX, giving women suffrage, went in effect, 1920

27 Friday

America's first oil well drilled near Titusville, Pennsylvania, 1859
President Lyndon B. Johnson born, 1908

28 Saturday

Work at Bureau of Printing and Engraving began, 5 employees, 1862

29 Sunday

Author Oliver Wendell Holmes born, 1809

August

Diary

A Balladine

She was the prettiest girl, I ween,
That mortal eyes had ever seen;
Her name is Anabel Christine,
Her bangs were curled with bandoline,
Her cheeks were smoothed with vaseline,
Her teeth were brushed with fine dentine,
Her lace was washed in coaline,
Her gloves were cleaned with gasoline,
She wore a dress of grenadine,
Looped over a skirt of brilliantine.
Her petticoat was bombazine,
Her foot was shod with a kid bottine,
Her wounds were healed with cosmoline.
She sailed away from Muscatine
In a ship they called brigantine.
She flirted with a gay marine
Till they reached th' Republic Argentine,
Where they were married by the Dean,
And lived on oleomargarine.

Cornelia Seabring Parker
From Scribner's Monthly, Volume XX, October 1880

92

September

Sun	Mon	Tue	Wed	Thu	Fri	Sat
				1	2	3	4
5	6	7	8	9	10	11
12	13	14	15	16	17	18
19	20	21	22	23	24	25
26	27	28	29	30		

Appointments

30 Monday

Actor Raymond Massey born, 1896
Henry Ford received patent for gasoline carburetor, 1898

31 Tuesday

Comedian Arthur Godfrey born, 1903

1 Wednesday

First Pullman sleeping car in operation, 1860
First training school for nurses,
New England Hospital, Boston, admitted 5 students, 1872

2 Thursday

V-J Day
Single tax economist Henry George born, 1839
Gold discoverd in the Black Hills, 1874

3 Friday

Revolutionary War ended with Treaty of Paris, 1783

4 Saturday

First transcontinental TV broadcast, 1951

5 Sunday

First Continental Congress met, 1774
Outlaw Jesse James born, 1847

August September

Diary

KENDALL MFG CO. PROVIDENCE. R.I.

Labor Day

Monday September 6

Today's weather

We, the undersigned,
   will help out with the chores;
We'll lend a hand, and even volunteer.
We'll ease the work of others—
   as they ease ours;
We'll do not only all we can,
   but with good cheer.

What We Did on Labor Day

A Memento of Labor Day Weekend

September

Sun	Mon	Tue	Wed	Thu	Fri	Sat
				1	2	3	4
5	6	7	8	9	10	11
12	13	14	15	16	17	18
19	20	21	22	23	24	25
26	27	28	29	30		

Appointments

6 Monday

Labor Day, U.S. & Canada
Pilgrims set sail from Plymouth, England, 1620

7 Tuesday

Grandma Moses born, 1860

8 Wednesday

Large blue-green patch found on supposedly all-red Mars, 1955

9 Thursday

California became the 31st state, 1850

10 Friday

Elias Howe's sewing machine patented, 1846

11 Saturday

Author William Sidney Porter (O. Henry) born, 1862

12 Sunday

Grandparents Day
Publisher Alfred Knopf born, 1893

"Slates and slate pencils have been banned from Boston schools by official dictum. The light gray mark on the only slightly darkened slate surface is pronounced very trying to the eye, and the operation of erasing, as most often practiced by children, is not only uncleanly, but unwholesome as well. So the slates have gone, and paper and pencils have come."

From The New York Times. *December 23, 1894*

September

"We make our own destinies. Providence furnishes the raw material only."

Uncle Esek, Century Magazine, 1885

Diary

September

Sun	Mon	Tue	Wed	Thu	Fri	Sat
			1	2	3	4
5	6	7	8	9	10	11
12	13	14	15	16	17	18
19	20	21	22	23	24	25
26	27	28	29	30		

Appointments

13 Monday

Henry Hudson sailed into mouth of Hudson River, 1609
General John Pershing born, 1860

14 Tuesday

Francis Scott Key wrote "The Star-Spangled Banner," 1814

15 Wednesday

President William H. Taft born, 1857

16 Thursday

Oliver Wendell Holmes wrote "Old Ironsides," 1830
TV personality Allen "Smile" Funt born, 1914

17 Friday

Citizenship Day
U.S. Constitution signed, 1787

18 Saturday

Rosh Hashana—Jewish New Year, A.M. 5743
Horse won race with Tom Thumb's locomotive, 1830

19 Sunday

Washington's Farewell Address published, 1796

A Lucky Thought

"A man in Ohio was pursued lately by a black snake. All at once it occurred to him, just as the reptile was preparing to jump at his throat, to run around a small birch tree which stood in his path, as tight as he could spring; he did so till he'd got the creature in a *snarl*, when stopping suddenly, he threw a back somerset, and the snake trying to follow him tied himself in a *hard knot*."

From The Crockett Almanacks, *originally published between 1835 and 1838 in Nashville. The scholarly opinion is that Davy Crockett never had anything to do with the Almanacks, beyond being the legendary inspiration for them.*

• • •

Rag-Weed

"Of our rag-weed not much can be set down that is complimentary, except that its name in the botany is *Ambrosia*, food of the gods. It must be the food of the gods if of anything, for, so far as I have observed, nothing terrestrial eats it, not even billygoats."

From "Notes of a Walker" by John Burroughs, in Scribner's Monthly, *May 1880*

September

A. Toad
Furniture
Dealer
stools a Specialty

Diary

Mother and Baby Quiz

Put a checkmark next to all the names which you think are incorrect.

MOTHERS	BABIES
☐ Owl	☐ Owlet
☐ Sow	☐ Piglet
☐ Elephant	☐ Elephaun
☐ Ewe	☐ Lamb
☐ Hippopotamus	☐ Hippette
☐ Bitch	☐ Puppy
☐ Queen Cat	☐ Kitten
☐ Hen	☐ Chick
☐ Mare	☐ Foal
☐ Racoon	☐ Racocoon
☐ Nanny-goat	☐ Kid
☐ Doe	☐ Fawn
☐ Crocodile	☐ Crocochild
☐ Bear	☐ Cub
☐ Frog	☐ Tadpole
☐ Cow	☐ Calf
☐ Tigress	☐ Cub

Animal Quiz Answers: Only Elephaun, Hippette, Racocoon and Crocochild are wrong.

September

Sun	Mon	Tue	Wed	Thu	Fri	Sat
				1	2	3	4
5	6	7	8	9	10	11
12	13	14	15	16	17	18
19	20	21	22	23	24	25
26	27	28	29	30		

Appointments

20 Monday

Patent leather first manufactured, 1819
Author Upton Sinclair born, 1878

21 Tuesday

America's first gasoline auto, built by Charles & Frank Duryea, driven in Springfield, Massachusetts, 1893

22 Wednesday

Emancipation Proclamation drafted, 1862

23 Thursday

Autumnal Equinox: fall begins 4:46 a.m. DST

24 Friday

Native American Day
Chief Justice John Marshall born, 1755

25 Saturday

First U.S. newspaper, "Publick Occurrences," published in Boston, 1690

26 Sunday

Poet T. S. Eliot born, 1888
Composer George Gershwin born, 1898

September

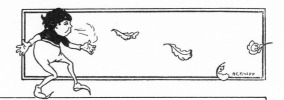

Diary

October

Sun	Mon	Tue	Wed	Thu	Fri	Sat
					1	2
3	4	5	6	7	8	9
10	11	12	13	14	15	16
17	18	19	20	21	22	23
24/31	25	26	27	28	29	30

Appointments

27 Monday

Yom Kippur—Day of Atonement
Cartoonist Thomas Nast born, 1840

28 Tuesday

TV host Ed Sullivan born, 1902
N.Y. woman arrested for smoking cigaret, 1904

29 Wednesday

Cowboy star Gene Autry born, 1907

30 Thursday

"Nautilus," first atomic submarine, commissioned, 1954

1 Friday

President Jimmy Carter born, 1924

2 Saturday

Succoth—"Feast of Tabernacles" Harvest Festival
Comedian Groucho Marx born, 1895

3 Sunday

Etiquette writer Emily Post born, 1873
First female U.S. Senator, Mrs. W. H. Felton, elected, 1922

"At one time a woman could hardly walk through the streets of San Francisco without having every one pause to gaze on her, and a child was so rare that once, in a theatre in the same city where a woman had taken her infant, when it began to cry, just as the orchestra began to play, a man in the pit cried out 'Stop those fiddles and let the baby cry. I hav'n't heard such a sound for ten years.' The audience applauded this sentiment, the orchestra stopped, and the baby continued its performance amid unbounded enthusiasm."

From The New-York News-Letter, *January-February 1890*

September *October*

Look-alike No. 6

October

Sun	Mon	Tue	Wed	Thu	Fri	Sat
					1	2
3	4	5	6	7	8	9
10	11	12	13	14	15	16
17	18	19	20	21	22	23
24/31	25	26	27	28	29	30

"No woman—so far as one can judge from printed collections—ever wrote more pleasant letters than do the American women. They have in their style English simplicity joined to French grace and spirit; when they are natural, they are best. They dress up little nothings with infinite drollery, they possess a keen apprehension of character, and they are, as a rule, good-tempered. I have no doubt the great Atlantic liners bring home in those leathern post-bags, thrown aboard just as the ship is ready to leave her dock, more wit in description from travelling American women, than could be found in the mails of any other nation."

From The House and Home, *1896*

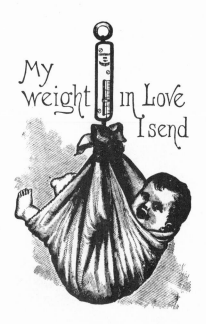

My weight in Love I send

Appointments
4 Monday
President Rutherford B. Hayes born, 1822
5 Tuesday
Universal Children's Day   *President Chester Alan Arthur born, 1830*
6 Wednesday
Inventor George Westinghouse born, 1846
7 Thursday
Poet James Whitcomb Riley born, 1849
8 Friday
Statesman John Hay born, 1838   *Aviator Eddie Rickenbacker born, 1890*
9 Saturday
Leif Ericsson Day
10 Sunday
International Letter Writing Week begins

October

Diary

October

Sun	Mon	Tue	Wed	Thu	Fri	Sat
					1	2
3	4	5	6	7	8	9
10	11	12	13	14	15	16
17	18	19	20	21	22	23
24/31	25	26	27	28	29	30

Thou no gods shalt have but me,
Before no idol bow the knee,
Take not the name of God in vain,
Nor dare the Sabbath day profane.
Give to thy parents honor due,
Take heed that thou no murder do.
Abstain from words and deeds unclean,
Steal not, for thou of God art seen.
Tell not a wilful lie, nor love it;
What is thy neighbor's do not covet.

"In dyeing artificial flowers the color is usually applied with the fingers, muslin, or paper; but the flowers may be simply dipped in the solution. *Blue.* Sulphate of indigo in solution. *Green.* Solution of distilled verdigris. *Lilac.* Liquid archil. *Red.* Carmine dissolved in carbonate of potash, or in spirits of hartshorn. *Violet.* Liquid archil mixed with a little salt of tartar. *Yellow.* Tincture of turmeric."

From Scammell's Universal Treasure-House, 1891

Appointments

11 Monday

Columbus Day observed nationally
Canadian Thanksgiving Day (see page 120)

12 Tuesday

Columbus landed in the West Indies, 1492
Columbus Day first celebrated, 1792

13 Wednesday

Cornerstone of White House laid, 1792

14 Thursday

First Mississippi & Ohio River steamboat, 1811
President Dwight D. Eisenhower born, 1890

15 Friday

Poetry Day

16 Saturday

Playwright Eugene O'Neill born, 1888

17 Sunday

22nd annual National Forest Products Week begins
Albert Einstein immigrated to the U.S., 1933

October

CLASS IN ECONOMY.

(OVER.)

October

Sun	Mon	Tue	Wed	Thu	Fri	Sat
					1	2
3	4	5	6	7	8	9
10	11	12	13	14	15	16
17	18	19	20	21	22	23
24/31	25	26	27	28	29	30

Swimming Turkeys

"When about to cross a river, [wild turkeys] select the highest eminences, that their flight may be the more certain; and here they sometimes remain for a day or more, as if for the purpose of consultation, or to be duly prepared for so hazardous a voyage. During this time the males *gobble* obstreperously, and strut with extraordinary importance, as if they would animate their companions, and inspire them with the utmost degree of hardihood. At length the assembled multitude mount to the tops of the highest trees, whence, at a signal note from a leader, the whole together wing their way towards the opposite shore.

"All the old and fat ones cross without difficulty, even when the river exceeds a mile in width; but the young and weak frequently fall short of the desired landing, and are forced to swim for their lives; this they do dextrously enough, spreading their tails for support, closing their wings to the body, and striking out forcibly and quick with their legs. When they approach the bank, with one violent effort they rise out of the water and reach the top of the bank."

From The Crockett Almanack, *1837*

Appointments

18 Monday

Hurricane Thanksgiving Day, Virgin Islands—hurricane season over
U.S. took formal possession of Alaska, 1867
Prime Minister Pierre E. Trudeau born, 1919

19 Tuesday

Martha Jefferson born, 1748
First balloon wedding, over Cincinnati, Ohio, 1874

20 Wednesday

President Coolidge coins "A chicken in every pot," 1928

21 Thursday

Poet Will Carleton born, 1845
Margaret B. Owen hit out 170 wpm on her typewriter. No errors, 1918

22 Friday

N.Y. Metropolitan Opera House opened with "Faust," 1883

23 Saturday

Swallows leave Capistrano, California
Comedian Johnny Carson born, 1925

24 Sunday

Daylight Savings ends: set clocks back
Mothers-in-Law Day
United Nations Day—UN chartered, 1945

October

Diary

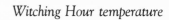

Witching Hour temperature

Halloween

Sunday October 31

We're batty about _____

_____

_____

_____

_____

_____

which *means that it's a* treat *to be with us.*

Trick-or-Treaters got _____

_____

_____

_____

_____

_____

at our house this Halloween.

Halloween Quiz

Cider is made from

Witches ride on

Jack o' Lanterns are

A witch's favorite pet is a

We counted _____ of 'em.

Ghosts: _____   Tramps: _____

Gypsies: _____   Pirates: _____

Others: _____

_____

_____

_____

The oldest person in the family recalls this Halloween trick from a long time ago:

October

Sun	Mon	Tue	Wed	Thu	Fri	Sat
					1	2
3	4	5	6	7	8	9
10	11	12	13	14	15	16
17	18	19	20	21	22	23
24/31	25	26	27	28	29	30

"The crooked course of the 'snake' fence is undeniably picturesque. Its 'zigzags' offer singularly choice retreats for great clumps of purple-stalked, red-stained, heavy-fruited poke-weed, for groups of yellow-brown *Osmunda* ferns, and for festoons of bitter-sweet, with orange pods split open to reveal their scarlet-coated seeds. No stone wall can yield such occasional vistas of meadow beyond, bright with golden-rod and aster, and framed by brilliant strands of blackberry vine. When its plants and shrubs and creepers are left quite unmolested, free to follow its devious course, to twine about its posts, or to peep confidingly over its topmost rails, then, I own, my loyalty begins to waver."

From According to Season
by Mrs. William Starr Dana, 1894

The vigil or eve of a feast is the day before it occurs. Hence Hallow-e'en is the eve of All Saints Day, a hallowed day.

Appointments

25 Monday

Nylon stockings first went on sale, 1940

26 Tuesday

Erie Canal dedicated, 1825
Singer Mahalia Jackson born, 1911

27 Wednesday

Navy Day—30th annual observance
President Theodore Roosevelt born, 1858

28 Thursday

Statue of Liberty unveiled, 1886

29 Friday

Stock Market collapsed, 1929

30 Saturday

President John Adams born, 1735
Orson Welles' simulated news broadcast,
"War of the Worlds," creates panic, 1938

31 Sunday

Halloween
National Magic Day—Houdini died, 1926
Nevada became the 36th state, 1864

October

Diary

Heavy Timbered Land

" 'Is the land well timbered?' inquired a person of a man who was offering a tract of land for sale. 'I vum,' replied the vendor, 'it is a most almighty piece of land, and so heavy timbered that a humming bird could not fly through it. As I was passing upon the road along side of it tother evening, I heard a loud cracking and crashing in the trees, so I looked to see what it was, and I'm darned if it were not the moon trying to git through the branches but 'twas so tarnation thick she couldn't do it, so down she went, and I had to go home in the dark."

From The Crockett Almanack, *1837*

"You may put the world down as a mob of fools, but don't forget this: it takes a smart man to beat them."
Uncle Esek, Century Magazine, *1885*

November

Sun	Mon	Tue	Wed	Thu	Fri	Sat
		1	2	3	4	5	6
7	8	9	10	11	12	13
14	15	16	17	18	19	20
21	22	23	24	25	26	27
28	29	30				

Appointments

1 Monday

All Saints Day

2 Tuesday

All Souls Day
President James K. Polk born, 1795;
President Warren G. Harding born, 1865
North Dakota & South Dakota became the 39th and 40th states, 1889

3 Wednesday

Poet William Cullen Bryant born, 1794
Jimmy Walker became Mayor of N.Y.C., 1925

4 Thursday

Humorist Will Rogers born, 1879
First air-conditioned automobile, 1939

5 Friday

Socialist Eugene V. Debs born, 1855

6 Saturday

Sadie Hawkins Day: Ask the man of your choice for a date
Basketball inventor James Naismith born, 1861

7 Sunday

Cartoonist Thomas Nast first used an elephant to symbolize Republicans, 1874

November

Diary

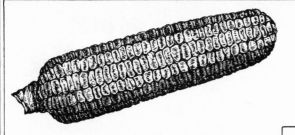

November

Sun	Mon	Tue	Wed	Thu	Fri	Sat
		1	2	3	4	5	6
7	8	9	10	11	12	13
14	15	16	17	18	19	20
21	22	23	24	25	26	27
28	29	30				

A Corn Husking Frolic
in the Buckeye State

"... The fashion of a husking is this: The corn was heaped up in a sort of hillock close to the granary, on which the young Ohioians and 'Buckeys' (the lasses of Ohio are all called 'Buckeys') seated themselves in pairs; while the old wives, and old farmers were posted around, doing little, but talking much. Now the laws of corn husking are, that for each *red* ear that a youth finds he is entitled to exact a kiss from his partner. There were two or three young Irishmen in the group, and I could observe the 'young rogues' kissing half a dozen times on the same ear. Each of them laid a red ear close by him, and after every two or three he'd husk up, he'd hold the redoubtable red one to the astonished eyes of the giggling lass who sate beside him, and inflicted the penalty. ... All agreed that there was more laughing and more kissing done at that than had been known at any corn husking frolic since the Declaration."

From The Crockett Almanacks, *originally published in* Nashville, 1835 to 1838.

A football field is frequently called a *gridiron* because of the white five-yard lines that cross it, which make it resemble a gridiron.

Appointments

8 Monday

Lewis & Clark reached the Pacific Ocean, 1804
Montana became the 41st state, 1889

9 Tuesday

Abolitionist Elijah P. Lovejoy born, 1802
First blackout—N.Y.C., New England, Canada—occurred, 1965

10 Wednesday

United States Marine Corps founded, 1775

11 Thursday

Veterans' Day & Remembrance Day
World War I ended, 1918
Washington became the 42nd state, 1889

12 Friday

Suffragist Elizabeth Cady Stanton born, 1815

13 Saturday

Indian Summer begins (lasts until the 20th)
Actor Edwin Booth born, 1833

14 Sunday

Mamie Eisenhower born, 1896

November

Diary

Look-alike No. 7

November

Sun Mon Tue Wed Thu Fri Sat
1 2 3 4 5 6
7 8 9 10 11 12 13
14 15 16 17 18 19 20
21 22 23 24 25 26 27
28 29 30

8th Wonder Engle Clock

"Grand in conception, beautiful in design, the Engle Clock stands unrivaled, the admiration of the World. It operates 48 moving figures—more than double the number produced by the Strasburgh Clock in Germany. They are made of wax, and are exceedingly artistic and life-like, Our Saviour and the Twelve Apostles being copied from the renowned painting by Leonardo Da Vinci. It also operates more dials, has more wonderful mechanism, and more delicate movements, beside being more beautifully designed and finished than any mechanical invention or work of art beneath the sun. With the appearance of Orpheus and Linus, we hear beautiful music from a pipe organ within one of its towers, while a mechanical fife at intervals plays inspiring patriotic airs. No description of tongue or pen can give any adequate idea of the perfection of this marvelous work, which must be seen and examined before it can be even imperfectly comprehended. It delights equally the child and the philosopher, and has given greater satisfaction to the American public than any exhibition ever placed before them."

A 19th century trade card

Appointments
15 Monday
Dr. A. Carrel discovers white corpuscles in blood, 1923
16 Tuesday
"Father of the Blues," composer W. C. Handy, born, 1873 *Oklahoma became the 46th state, 1907*
17 Wednesday
America's first clock patent awarded to Eli Terry, 1797 *Suez Canal opened, 1869*
18 Thursday
Conductor Eugene Ormandy born, 1899 *First Mickey Mouse movie, "Steamboat Willie," shown in N.Y.C., 1928*
19 Friday
Puerto Rico Discovery Day *Explorer George Rogers Clark born, 1752* *President James A. Garfield born, 1831*
20 Saturday
Canadian Premier Sir Wilfred Laurier born, 1841
21 Sunday
American Education Week begins *North Carolina became the 12th state 1789*

November

Diary

Look-alike No. 8

May everyone you hold most dear,
Share with you Thanksgiving cheer.

Thanksgiving Day

Monday October 11 in Canada   Thursday November 25 in U.S.A.

Today's weather

A Prayer of Thanksgiving
To Be Read at Dinner

We Spent Thanksgiving Day This Way

Written by

Appetizers & Soups

Salads

Main Course

Desserts

*The Names of Those
Who Shared This Day*

A Memento of Thanksgiving Day

All in a Day's Work

"An *astronomical day* begins at noon, and is counted from the first to the 24th hour. A *civil day* commences at midnight, and is counted from the first to the 12th hour. A *nautical day* is counted as a civil day, but commences, like an astronomical day, at noon."

From Marshall's Almanac, *1890*

Bon Appetit!

"Winter hath his birds; some of them such tiny bodies, that one wonders how they withstand the giant cold—but they do. Birds live on highly concentrated food—the fine seeds of weeds and grasses, and the eggs and larvae of insects. Such food must be very stimulating and heating. A gizzard full of ants, for instance, what spiced and seasoned extract is equal to that? Think what virtue there must be in an ounce of gnats or mosquitoes, or in the fine mysterious food the chicakee and brown-creeper gather in the winter woods."

John Burroughs, in Scribner's Monthly, *August 1876*

November

Sun Mon Tue Wed Thu Fri Sat
　　　1　2　3　4　5　6
7　8　9　10 11 12 13
14 15 16 17 18 19 20
21 22 23 24 25 26 27
28 29 30

Appointments

22 Monday

Feast of Saint Cecilia
Musician Hoagy Carmichael born, 1899

23 Tuesday

President Franklin Pierce born, 1804
Comedian Harpo Marx born, 1893

24 Wednesday

President Zachary Taylor born, 1784
Piano rag composer Scott Joplin born, 1868

25 Thursday

Thanksgiving
Racial segregation banned on interstate trains & buses, 1955

26 Friday

Sojourner Truth Day
George Washington proclaimed the 26th as Thanksgiving Day, 1789

27 Saturday

Statesman Robert R. Livingston born, 1746

28 Sunday

Advent Sunday
First automobile race, Chicago to Waukegan held, 1895

November

Diary

LOOK Mama!
BED ROOM SUITES.
Other Dealer's Prices, $30.
Our Price, 20.
Net Saving, $10.
AT
E. E. ENGLISH,
518 & 520 Perry Street,
Trenton, N. J.

A Recipe for the Cholera
"Eat two cucumbers, dressed or raw, as you prefer; then take a quart of blackberries, four green corn, four young potatoes mashed, a lobster or a crab, some ice water, and wash the whole down with a quart of buttermilk, and you will shortly have a touch of the real thing."
From The Crockett Almanack, *1837*

"I don't believe in special providences. When a mule kicks a man, and knocks him anywhere from eight to twenty feet off, I don't lay it to the Lord; I say to myself, That man got a little too near the mule."
Uncle Esek, Century Magazine, *1885*

December

Sun	Mon	Tue	Wed	Thu	Fri	Sat
				1	2	3	4
5	6	7	8	9	10	11
12	13	14	15	16	17	18
19	20	21	22	23	24	25
26	27	28	29	30	31	

Appointments

29 Monday

Author Louisa May Alcott born, 1832
Lieutenant Commander Byrd flies over South Pole, 1930

30 Tuesday

Feast of Saint Andrew
Author Samuel Clemens (Mark Twain) born, 1835

1 Wednesday

Author Rex Stout born, 1886
Christmas Seals first sold, 1908

2 Thursday

Pan American Health Day
Monroe Doctrine announced, 1823
Opera singer Maria Callas born, 1923

3 Friday

Illinois became the 21st state, 1818

4 Saturday

American Antislavery Society formed, 1833

5 Sunday

President Martin Van Buren born, 1782

Diary

High Kicker at Mine.

Frankness

"Take a doughnut, my dear,—take two."
  The visitor looked with a wistful eye
But not at the doughnuts—ah, no!
  Her wishes were centred on pie:
"I can get doughnuts at home,"
  The little girl said with a sigh.

Edith M. Thomas, 1895

". . . An outcry is being made now in civilized cities against the large round flat hats worn by fashionable ladies. There is no doubt that these hats interfere with the comfort of theatre goers. One of them is alone sufficient to shut off the view of the entire stage from half a dozen men. So numerous are these hats that perhaps three quarters of the audience at any particular theatre does not obtain a single glimpse of the play."

From The New York Times, *January 5, 1882*

December

Sun	Mon	Tue	Wed	Thu	Fri	Sat
			1	2	3	4
5	6	7	8	9	10	11
12	13	14	15	16	17	18
19	20	21	22	23	24	25
26	27	28	29	30	31	

Appointments

6 Monday

St. Nicholas' Day
Poet Joyce Kilmer born, 1886

7 Tuesday

Delaware became the 1st state, 1787
Pearl Harbor bombed, 1941

8 Wednesday

Feast of the Immaculate Conception
Humorist James Thurber born, 1894

9 Thursday

"Uncle Remus" author Joel Chandler Harris born, 1848

10 Friday

Human Rights Day
Mississippi became the 20th state, 1817
Poet Emily Dickinson born, 1830

11 Saturday

Hanukkah—Jewish "Festival of Lights"
Indiana became the 19th state, 1816

12 Sunday

Pennsylvania became the 2nd state, 1787
Singer Frank Sinatra born, 1915

December

Diary

December

Sun	Mon	Tue	Wed	Thu	Fri	Sat
			1	2	3	4
5	6	7	8	9	10	11
12	13	14	15	16	17	18
19	20	21	22	23	24	25
26	27	28	29	30	31	

It's almost Christmas
It's almost here
The holidays are very near
It's almost New Year
It's almost the first
If they don't come soon
I'm gonna burst.

By Mike Billingsley
Patrick Henry Elementary, Alexandria, Virginia

"Hello! This is Squaw Gap!"

The first complete sentence was transmitted over a telephone on March 10, 1876. By 1877, telephones were being leased in pairs so that the two people at either end of the line could talk to each other. They couldn't call anyone else. Probably the only people in Squaw Gap, North Dakota, were Indians, but by 1909 there were enough people homesteading there, in the gap between the buttes, for there to be a schoolhouse. The children going to that school grew up, and their children grew up, and around 1948 they started trying to get phone service for the community. Finally, Reservation Telephone Cooperative, a rural North Dakota system, agreed to put 93 phones into Squaw Gap. The first call was made December 15, 1971, to the Secretary of Agriculture, Earl Butz, and after that phones began ringing all over the community, as neighbor called neighbor, and as people called faraway friends and relatives. There's still a schoolhouse; there's a community hall; and the Reservation Dialhouse, from where the magic connections are made, is going into its second decade. The gap in the buttes will never again seem so vast.

Appointments
13 Monday
St. Lucia's Day
First savings bank in U.S. chartered, 1817
14 Tuesday
Alabama became the 22nd state, 1819
Senator Margaret Chase Smith born, 1897
15 Wednesday
Bill of Rights Day—Bill of Rights went into effect, 1791
Phone service came to Squaw Gap, N.D., 1971
16 Thursday
Composer Ludwig von Beethoven born, 1770
Anthropologist Margaret Mead born, 1901
17 Friday
Pan American Aviation Day
Orville Wright, then Wilbur, flew at Kittyhawk, 1903
18 Saturday
New Jersey became the 3rd state, 1787
Amendment XIII, abolishing slavery, ratified, 1865
19 Sunday
Benjamin Franklin first published "Poor Richard's Alamanac," 1732
Christmas greetings from President Eisenhower,
first voice broadcast from space satellite, 1958

December

Diary

Christmas

Saturday December 25

Today's weather

Call for
SCHUMACHER'S
Parched Farinose
THE TYPE OF A PERFECT FOOD
(OVER.)

This is How We Spent Christmas Eve

*The Names of Those
Who Shared the Day Together*

The Christmas Carols We Like Best

MENU

Appetizers & Soups

Salads

Main Course

Sauces & Relishes

Desserts

A Memento of Our Christmas

I don't object, not I, to know
My sires were monkeys, if 't was so;
I touch my ear's collusive tip
And own the poor-relationship.
That apes of various shapes and sizes
Contained their germs that all the prizes
Of senate, pulpit, camp, and bar win
May give us hopes that sweeten Darwin.
Who knows but from our loins may spring
      (Long hence) some winged
sweet-throated thing
As much superior to us
As we to Cynocephalus?

From Credidimus Jovem Regnare, *James Russell Lowell*

Love-Light Best of All
Christmas lights may gleam and glow,
  And Christmas joy bells ring,
Christmas mirth and joy may flow,
  And happy voices sing:
Christmas trees with bending boughs
  May stately stand so tall,
But Christmas light within the heart
  Is the light that's best for all.

For joy and gladness must abide,
  Good cheer our hearts must fill—
And love must flow, a boundless tide,
  And peace and kind good will.
So let the bells ring sweet and clear,
  Your gifts and garlands bring,
But know of all your Christmas cheer
  Love is the greatest thing.

Elizabeth Clarke Hardy, 1911

December

Sun	Mon	Tue	Wed	Thu	Fri	Sat
				1	2	3	4
5	6	7	8	9	10	11
12	13	14	15	16	17	18
19	20	21	22	23	24	25
26	27	28	29	30	31	

Appointments

20 Monday

Shoe rationing ended, 1945

21 Tuesday

Winter Solstice: winter begins 11:39 a.m. EST
Jules Verne's Phileas Fogg completes round-the-world trip, 1872

22 Wednesday

First gorilla born in captivity, Columbus, Ohio, 1957

23 Thursday

Mormon prophet Joseph Smith born, 1805

24 Friday

Christmas Eve
Methodist Church organized in America, 1784
Patriot Benjamin Rush born, 1745

25 Saturday

Christmas Day
Nurse Clara Barton born, 1821
Jazz great Cab Calloway born, 1907

26 Sunday

Boxing Day & St. Stephen's Day

December

Diary

FOR A HAPPY NEW YEAR

I Know Not Why

I lift mine eyes against the sky,
The clouds are weeping, so am I;
I lift mine eyes again on high,
The sun is smiling, so am I.
Why do I smile? Why do I weep?
I do not know; it lies too deep.

I hear the winds of autumn sigh,
They break my heart, they make me cry;
I hear the birds of lovely spring,
My hopes revive, I help them sing.
Why do I sing? Why do I cry?
It lies so deep, I know not why.

Morris Rosenfeld

December

Sun	Mon	Tue	Wed	Thu	Fri	Sat
				1	2	3	4
5	6	7	8	9	10	11
12	13	14	15	16	17	18
19	20	21	22	23	24	25
26	27	28	29	30	31	

Appointments

27 Monday

French scientist Louis Pasteur born, 1822
Radio City Music Hall opened, 1932

28 Tuesday

Holy Innocents Day
Iowa became the 29th state, 1846
President Woodrow Wilson born, 1856

29 Wednesday

President Andrew Johnson born, 1808
Texas became the 28th state, 1845

30 Thursday

Philanthropist Simon Guggenheim born, 1867
Canadian humorist Stephen Leacock born, 1869
Massa, gorilla at Philadelphia Zoo, born, 1930

31 Friday

New Year's Eve
Road Runners Club of N.Y.C. Midnight Race in Central Park

1 Saturday

New Year's Day, 1983

2 Sunday

Patriot Paul Revere born, 1735

December _January_

Look-alike No. 9

Language of Flowers

"A very charming and interesting method of communicating thought is by the aid of flowers, their language and sentiment being understood by the parties who present them. . . . An extended and sometimes important correspondence may be carried on by the presentation of bouquets, single flowers and even leaves; the charm of this interchange of thought largely consisting in the romance attendant upon an expression of sentiment in a partially disguised and hidden language."

From Hill's Manual of Social & Business Forms, 1905

Acacia *Friendship.*

Agrimony *Thankfulness. Gratitude.*

Amaryllis *Pride. Timidity.*

Anemone *Forsaken.*

Azalea *Temperance.*

Bachelor's Button *Hope. Single blessedness.*

Basil *Give me your good wishes.*

Bay Rhododendron *Danger. Beware.*

Bindweed *Humility. Night.*

Birch *Grace. Elegance.*

Bluebell *Constancy.*

Borage *Abruptness.*

Box *Stoicism.*

Broom *Neatness. Humility*

Buckbean *Calm repose.*

Bulrush *Indiscretion. Docility.*

Buttercup *Riches. Memories of childhood.*

Cabbage *Profit.*

Camomile *Energy in adversity.*

Carnation *Pure and deep love.*

China Aster *Love of variety.*

Clover, Four leaved *Be mine.*

Cloves *Dignity.*

Cockle *Vain is beauty without merit.*

Cowslip *Pensiveness. Native grace.*

Daffodil *Unrequited love.*

Dandelion *Coquetry. Rustic oracle.*

Dittany of Crete *Birth.*

Dogwood *Durability.*

Elder *Zealousness.*

Endive *Frugality.*

Fern *Sincerity.*

Fir *Elevation.*

Flax *Domestic industry. Fate.*

Gentian *Intrinsic worth.*

Geranium, Rose *I prefer you.*

Grape vine *Intemperance.*

Hibiscus *Delicate beauty.*

Heath *Solitude.*

Horse Chestnut *Luxury.*

Ivy *Fidelity. Marriage.*

Jonquil *I desire a return of affection.*

Juniper *Succor. Protection.*

King-cups *Desire of riches.*

Larkspur, Purple *Haughtiness.*

Laurel, Mountain *Ambition.*

Lavender *Mistrust.*

Lotus *Recantation.*

Magnolia *Love of nature.*

Mandrake *Rarity.*

Marshmallow *Beneficence.*

Mint *Virtue.*

Myrrh *Gladness.*

Nasturtium *Patriotism. Splendor.*

Nightshade *Truth.*

Oak *Hospitality. Bravery.*

Oleander *Beware.*

Osmunda *Reverie. Dreams.*

Peppermint *Warmth of feeling.*

Pink, Red Double *Pure and ardent love.*

Plum, Wild *Independence.*

Primrose *Modest worth. Silent love.*

Rosebud, White *Too young to love.*

Rose, Musk *Capricious beauty.*

Rosemary *Your presence revives me.*

Saxifrage, Mossy *Affection.*

Sensitive Plant *Delicate feelings.*

Sweet Basil *Good feelings.*

Thyme *Activity.*

Turnip *Charity.*

Wall Flower *Fidelity in misfortune.*

Yarrow *Cure for heartache.*

Yew *Sadness.*

Language of Precious Stones

Language of Precious Stones
"The ancients attributed marvellous properties to many of the precious stones, and particular gems have been marked by their own distinguishing fables. The same notions have more or less continued down to times not long past. We give in tabular form the different months and the stones sacred to them, with their respective legendary meaning. It has been customary among lovers and friends to notice the significance attached to the various stones in making birthday, engagement and wedding presents."

The preceding and following from Marshall's Almanac, 1890

January	*Garnet.* Constancy and fidelity in every engagement.
February	*Amethyst.* Preventive against violent passions.
March	*Bloodstone.* Courage, wisdom and firmness in affection.
April	*Sapphire.* Frees from enchantment; denotes repentance.
May	*Emerald.* Discovers false friends and insures true love.
June	*Agate.* Insures long life, health and prosperity.
July	*Ruby.* Discovers poison; corrects evils resulting from mistaken friendship.
August	*Sardonyx.* Insures conjugal fidelity.
September	*Chrysolite.* Frees from evil passions and sadness of the mind.
October	*Opal.* Denotes hope and sharpens the sight and faith of the possessor.
November	*Topaz.* Fidelity and friendship; prevents bad dreams.
December	*Turquoise.* Prosperity in love.

We append a list of precious stones in common use not included in the above:

Moonstone. Protects from harm and danger.

Diamond. Faith; innocence; virginity.

Heliotrope. Causes the wearer to walk invisible.

Pearl. Purity; gives clearness to physical and mental sight.

Catseye. Possesses the virtue of enriching the wearer.

Gifts for Wedding Anniversaries

It has long been the custom to give anniversary gifts. As it is expected that gold be given to the celebrating couple on their 50th—Golden—Anniversary, so it has evolved that all the anniversaries up to the fifteenth have special gifts, and every fifth one beyond that also has an appropriate gift. Those couples who celebrate beyond their 75th Anniversary surely have the most precious gift of all—their lasting love for each other.

Anniversary	Gift	Anniversary	Gift
1st	Paper or plastic	11th	Steel
2nd	Cotton	12th	Linen or silk
3rd	Leather	13th	Lace
4th	Silk or linen	14th	Ivory or agate
5th	Wood	15th	Crystal
6th	Iron	20th	Porcelain or china
7th	Wool, copper or brass	25th	Silver
8th	Electric appliances or bronze	30th	Pearl
9th	Pottery	35th	Coral or jade
10th	Tin or aluminum	40th	Ruby or garnet
		45th	Sapphire or tourmaline
		50th	Gold
		55th	Emerald or turquoise
		60th	Diamond
		75th	Diamond

Weddings & Anniversaries

Love makes the world go 'round,
    And so the poets and the songsters say.
Here, in future, will be found
    Records of all friends' wedding days.

Graduations, Promotions & Milestone Days

Throughout the year come special days,
That stand out like a star in midnight sky;
Therefore, be ready with your praise,
Make careful note, ere you forget.
A letter with a thoughtful phrase,
Sent to a friend—nothing better says "I care!"

Our Family Birthdays

Birthdays come but once a year,
Leap birthdays once in four.
May all the birthdays listed here
Be followed by many more.

Our Friends' Birthdays

Time was, you could send a birthday card in an envelope of just about any size and shape. Now, if you want to send *old* cards, put them in new envelopes. Remember that the post office requires that an envelope be at least 3½″ high, 5″ long, rectangular in shape, and at least .007″ thick (the thickness of a thin postcard). In other words, don't send a tissue-paper thin card or letter—it will jam the machines.

1982

January
Sun	Mon	Tue	Wed	Thu	Fri	Sat
					1	2
3	4	5	6	7	8	9
10	11	12	13	14	15	16
17	18	19	20	21	22	23
24/31	25	26	27	28	29	30

February
Sun	Mon	Tue	Wed	Thu	Fri	Sat
	1	2	3	4	5	6
7	8	9	10	11	12	13
14	15	16	17	18	19	20
21	22	23	24	25	26	27
28						

March
Sun	Mon	Tue	Wed	Thu	Fri	Sat
	1	2	3	4	5	6
7	8	9	10	11	12	13
14	15	16	17	18	19	20
21	22	23	24	25	26	27
28	29	30	31			

April
Sun	Mon	Tue	Wed	Thu	Fri	Sat
				1	2	3
4	5	6	7	8	9	10
11	12	13	14	15	16	17
18	19	20	21	22	23	24
25	26	27	28	29	30	

May
Sun	Mon	Tue	Wed	Thu	Fri	Sat
						1
2	3	4	5	6	7	8
9	10	11	12	13	14	15
16	17	18	19	20	21	22
23/30	24/31	25	26	27	28	29

June
Sun	Mon	Tue	Wed	Thu	Fri	Sat
		1	2	3	4	5
6	7	8	9	10	11	12
13	14	15	16	17	18	19
20	21	22	23	24	25	26
27	28	29	30			

July
Sun	Mon	Tue	Wed	Thu	Fri	Sat
				1	2	3
4	5	6	7	8	9	10
11	12	13	14	15	16	17
18	19	20	21	22	23	24
25	26	27	28	29	30	31

August
Sun	Mon	Tue	Wed	Thu	Fri	Sat
1	2	3	4	5	6	7
8	9	10	11	12	13	14
15	16	17	18	19	20	21
22	23	24	25	26	27	28
29	30	31				

September
Sun	Mon	Tue	Wed	Thu	Fri	Sat
			1	2	3	4
5	6	7	8	9	10	11
12	13	14	15	16	17	18
19	20	21	22	23	24	25
26	27	28	29	30		

October
Sun	Mon	Tue	Wed	Thu	Fri	Sat
					1	2
3	4	5	6	7	8	9
10	11	12	13	14	15	16
17	18	19	20	21	22	23
24/31	25	26	27	28	29	30

November
Sun	Mon	Tue	Wed	Thu	Fri	Sat
	1	2	3	4	5	6
7	8	9	10	11	12	13
14	15	16	17	18	19	20
21	22	23	24	25	26	27
28	29	30				

December
Sun	Mon	Tue	Wed	Thu	Fri	Sat
			1	2	3	4
5	6	7	8	9	10	11
12	13	14	15	16	17	18
19	20	21	22	23	24	25
26	27	28	29	30	31	

1983

January
Sun	Mon	Tue	Wed	Thu	Fri	Sat
						1
2	3	4	5	6	7	8
9	10	11	12	13	14	15
16	17	18	19	20	21	22
23/30	24/31	25	26	27	28	29

February
Sun	Mon	Tue	Wed	Thu	Fri	Sat
		1	2	3	4	5
6	7	8	9	10	11	12
13	14	15	16	17	18	19
20	21	22	23	24	25	26
27	28					

March
Sun	Mon	Tue	Wed	Thu	Fri	Sat
		1	2	3	4	5
6	7	8	9	10	11	12
13	14	15	16	17	18	19
20	21	22	23	24	25	26
27	28	29	30	31		

April
Sun	Mon	Tue	Wed	Thu	Fri	Sat
					1	2
3	4	5	6	7	8	9
10	11	12	13	14	15	16
17	18	19	20	21	22	23
24	25	26	27	28	29	30

May
Sun	Mon	Tue	Wed	Thu	Fri	Sat
1	2	3	4	5	6	7
8	9	10	11	12	13	14
15	16	17	18	19	20	21
22	23	24	25	26	27	28
29	30	31				

June
Sun	Mon	Tue	Wed	Thu	Fri	Sat
			1	2	3	4
5	6	7	8	9	10	11
12	13	14	15	16	17	18
19	20	21	22	23	24	25
26	27	28	29	30		

July
Sun	Mon	Tue	Wed	Thu	Fri	Sat
					1	2
3	4	5	6	7	8	9
10	11	12	13	14	15	16
17	18	19	20	21	22	23
24/31	25	26	27	28	29	30

August
Sun	Mon	Tue	Wed	Thu	Fri	Sat
	1	2	3	4	5	6
7	8	9	10	11	12	13
14	15	16	17	18	19	20
21	22	23	24	25	26	27
28	29	30	31			

September
Sun	Mon	Tue	Wed	Thu	Fri	Sat
				1	2	3
4	5	6	7	8	9	10
11	12	13	14	15	16	17
18	19	20	21	22	23	24
25	26	27	28	29	30	

October
Sun	Mon	Tue	Wed	Thu	Fri	Sat
						1
2	3	4	5	6	7	8
9	10	11	12	13	14	15
16	17	18	19	20	21	22
23/30	24/31	25	26	27	28	29

November
Sun	Mon	Tue	Wed	Thu	Fri	Sat
		1	2	3	4	5
6	7	8	9	10	11	12
13	14	15	16	17	18	19
20	21	22	23	24	25	26
27	28	29	30			

December
Sun	Mon	Tue	Wed	Thu	Fri	Sat
				1	2	3
4	5	6	7	8	9	10
11	12	13	14	15	16	17
18	19	20	21	22	23	24
25	26	27	28	29	30	31

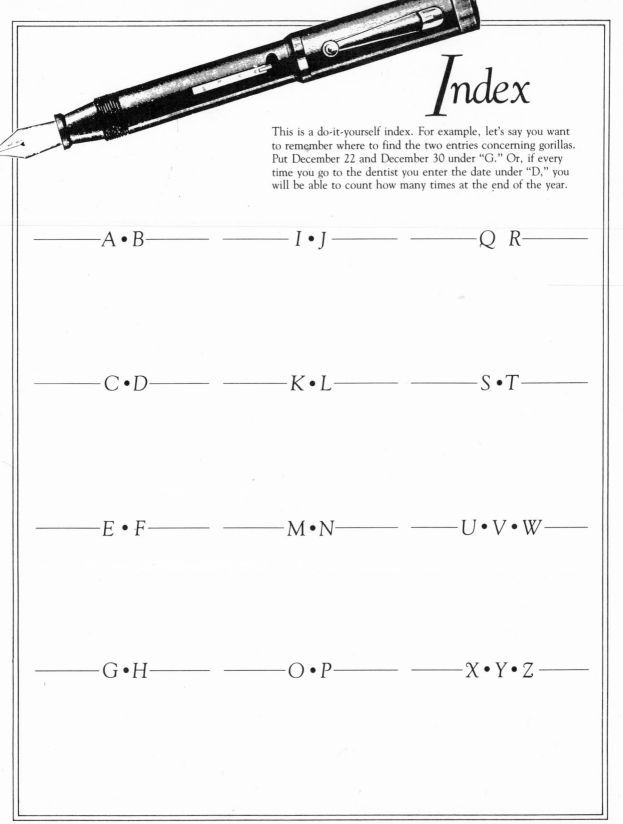

*I*ndex

This is a do-it-yourself index. For example, let's say you want to remember where to find the two entries concerning gorillas. Put December 22 and December 30 under "G." Or, if every time you go to the dentist you enter the date under "D," you will be able to count how many times at the end of the year.

A • B   I • J   Q R

C • D   K • L   S • T

E • F   M • N   U • V • W

G • H   O • P   X • Y • Z